Organic Grassland

by

Jon Newton

CHALCOMBE PUBLICATIONS

First published in Great Britain in 1993 by Chalcombe Publications
Painshall, Church Lane, Welton
Lincoln, UK. LN2 3LT

Reprinted 1999, 2001

ISBN 0 948617 28 4

Reprinted in Great Britain by Ruddocks Colour Printers, Lincoln.

Contents

For Máire.

Preface

The aim of this book is to bring together as much relevant knowledge as exists on the management of organic grassland. Organic agriculture has been almost completely overlooked by the major research bodies in Britain, and at the same time organic farmers have been accused of basing their practice on superstition and "Old Wives Tales".

The British government is unlikely to provide adequate funding for research into 'organic' problems, but paradoxically there is Treasury money available for set-aside, and growing public interest in conservation and extensive agriculture.

Organic farmers are strongly committed to their principles: they regard their soil, crops and animals as resources to be cared for in terms of sustainability, animal welfare and human health, in addition to being economically viable. The central theme of this book is organic grassland, for grassland is one of the major natural resources of Britain. Along with Ireland, Britain has the most favourable climate in Europe, for providing grassland products such as milk, beef, lamb and wool. Against this background, organic grassland farming deserves to be encouraged, assisted and appreciated. This book is designed to increase awareness of organic practice and to provice technical information for those involved.

I wish to acknowledge permission from (i) Blackwells to reproduce illustrations from 'The Identification of Weed Seedlings of Farm and Garden', by R.J. Chancellor, amd (ii) Suttons for allowing me to reproduce drawings of grasses and legumes from 'Permanent and Temporary pastures' by M.J. Sutton, M.H.F. Sutton and J. Percival.

Finally I would like to thank Mike Wilkinson for his encouragement and Linda Heard for typing the script.

Jon Newton.
Exeter,
November 1992.

Foreword

The publication of 'Organic Grassland' is a significant step in the development of organic agriculture in the UK. Despite its central role on many organic farms in Britain, organic grassland has received less attention from researchers and writers than some areas of production. Mr Newton's good, sound text on the essential components of organic grassland and its management redresses the balance.

Jon Newton is a grassland specialist who has long and extensive experience involving research into grassland and legume-based systems. Unlike many researchers, however, he has a grasp of the practicalities which enables him to impart information without being too academic. His experience of organic farming through the Organic Sheep Society and the Organic Advisory Service provides him with insights not usually open to those with a background in 'conventional' agricultural research.

There are an increasing number of publications setting out to give information on organic production: some are valuable, but alas many are not. As the move away from intensive production gathers pace, there will undoubtedly be more. This book will find a place at the better end of the range and will reward any farmer, student or researcher who has a serious interest in organic grassland.

Lawrence Woodward,
Coordinator, Elm Farm Research Centre,
Hamstead Marshall, Newbury, Berkshire, UK.

Chapter 1

The Case for Organic Grassland

Food Safety

The public is becoming increasingly worried about the safety of its food, the stability of the soil and the pollution of drinking water. More than 50 years ago Professor Stapledon, the first director of the Welsh Plant Breeding Station, wrote about the likelihood that fresh food would be 'proved essential to robust health'. In the last few years there has been the radioactive fallout from Chernobyl, which contaminated large areas of grassland in Cumbria and North Wales and produced a ban on the sale of livestock for human consumption from those areas. There has been bovine spongiform encephalopathy (BSE) or 'mad cow' disease caused, so it is thought, by the feeding of offals to cows, and there has been the slaughter of thousands of poultry believed to be infecting humans with salmonella.

People are worried about the safety of what they eat and drink and at the same time the agricultural policy of the European Community Countries has led to the expensive stock-piling of beef, butter, milk and wine. European farmers, like their American counterparts, are being paid to take land out of production: to reduce the size of their dairy herds, or on beef and sheep farms to farm more extensively.

In 1990, for the first time, truly organic meat carried a worthwhile premium and though this premium fluctuated in 1991-2, organic produce still sells for more than conventional meat. As conventional farmers are forced to sell their farms, squeezed by high interest rates on their overdrafts and falling prices for their livestock, the prospect of achieving a better price for their products has led them to consider the organic option.

These three factors, the desire of the public for safe food, overproduction of livestock products in Europe, and reduced profits, has led to the present surge of interest in organic agriculture. The goal of agricultural research and development for the last 50 years has been to intensify and to increase production per animal, per unit of land and per worker. The green revolution in India, China and Malaysia has been based on higher yielding rice, but on a rice variety that requires fertiliser and irrigation, often at the expense of soil structure. In Europe and North America overproduction is abundantly obvious and a switch to quality rather than quantity is a revolutionary change which has profound consequences. There has been a hiatus, a loss of purpose. What is now the goal of research and development, if it is not the production of more?

4

What is organic food production?

If organic agriculture is to become the beneficiary of government funding and research then organic food production must be defined and there will be an increase in organic food in the shops (as has been forecast). There have been many attempts at defining organic, and there are halfway houses such as 'conservation' grade and 'natural'. The most widely accepted definition of 'organic' is that put forward by the International Federation of Organic Agriculture Movements (IFOAM) in eleven points:

1. to produce food of high nutritional quality in sufficient quantity;
2. to work with natural systems rather than seeking to dominate them;
3. to encourage and enhance biological codes within the farming system, involving micro-organisms, soil flora and fauna, plants and animals;
4. to maintain and increase the long-term fertility of soils;
5. to use as far as possible renewable resources in locally organised agricultural systems;
6. to work as much as possible within the closed system with regard to organic matter and nutrient elements;
7. to give all livestock conditions of life that allow them to perform all aspects of their innate behaviour;
8. to avoid all forms of pollution that may result from agricultural techniques;
9. to maintain the genetic diversity of the agricultural system and its surroundings, including the protection of plant and wildlife habitats;
10. to allow agricultural producers an adequate return and satisfaction from their work including a safe working environment;
11. to consider the wider social and ecological impact of the farming system.

The proper management of grassland relates to the first 9 elements and if managed well then grassland will contribute to 10 and 11. It has been said that it is only possible to produce good grass after a preliminary period in arable. The reverse is, however, probably the truer dictum - to produce good arable crops - first make good grass! On the more difficult land, in all parts of the world, the corner-stone in improving productivity is the leguminous plant.

Converting to an organic system should not be seen as withholding quick and harmful solutions to problems. Nor is it a question of going back in time and ignoring the scientific understanding that has been developed. But it is a case of searching for research results that can be related to organic problems, which have been largely ignored whilst intensification and higher output have been the underlying themes of scientific programmes.

When organic food is bought in the shops then the method of production should be clearly defined. This is the purpose of UKROFS, the United Kingdom Register of Organic Food Standards. UKROFS draws together the various standards promulgated by such bodies as the Soil Association and Organic Farmers and Growers.

Although the organic acreage is forecast to grow from 1 to 10% in the next ten years, it is still a minority movement and needs to be united in the face of powerful agro-chemical opposition.

The issue of grass productivity

Grassland farmers seeking the organic label for their grassland face a number of problems. The chief of these is the reduction of stocking rate when artificial fertilisers, particularly nitrogen, are no longer available to boost grass production. A reduction in stocking rate means less milk, less beef and less lamb being sold from the farm. No one wants organic to become synonymous with poverty. The organic farmer has two options, one is to lessen his costs and the second is to increase the productivity of his grassland by good organic management, which will almost certainly involve the use of more legumes. One of the main objectives of this book is to examine methods of assessing grassland productivity and to point the way to increasing profitability from grass for the organic farmer. This is not the same as intensifying by importing fertility or keeping the grazing animal short of grass. Dry matter output from grassland can vary by a factor of at least eight (1.2 to 8.5 t DM per hectare per annum) and ewe size can vary by a factor of three (30 to 90 kg). It is no more intensive, nutritionally, to keep thirty small ewes per ha on a good field than three large ewes per ha in a poor field. Farmers must be encouraged to consider grass as a crop, which like wheat or sugar beet, will have a definite and measurable yield. It is not an amorphous green carpet, and it can be variable in performance. If the organic farmer is going to follow the points laid down by IFOAM then he must understand grassland and use it to farm profitably.

Where pastures are of low productivity, either because they have been taken for hay continuously with no attempt to replace the nutrients, or because they are deficient in legumes, or on poor soil, then yield is likely to be only about 1 t of dry matter per hectare per annum, sufficient only to support four small ewes per ha. Improving yield on these neglected fields by only 1 t will double the productivity and double the liveweight output, enough to fatten a yearling steer. Both Friend Sykes at Chantry on the Wiltshire Downs and Newman Turner at Goosegreen in Somerset chronicle the gradual increase in overall fertility of their farms, which were described as 'exhausted' and 'dying' when first acquired.

On all-grass farms the control of intestinal parasites is difficult, particularly if there is only a small area of the farm suitable for conservation and if there are more sheep livestock units than cattle, which is often the case. This makes the organisation of a clean grazing system virtually impossible to implement, because the permanent pasture area will be grazed by sheep every year. The conventional farmer will need to use anthelmintics on a regular basis but the organic farmer cannot rely on chemicals routinely. Under these circumstances it is often suggested that the stocking rate of the sheep should be reduced below the carrying capacity of the grassland, to reduce the concentration of the parasites. But if the grassland is under-utilised less desirable grass species may increase. There is also the important factor that sheep tend to select herbage from their favourite areas, this results in a much heavier local stocking rate on these grazing areas and a much lower stocking rate on the neglected areas, but it doesn't reduce the risk of parasitic infection. This problem will be dealt with in a later chapter.

The stimulation of early pasture growth (early bite) by the application of nitrogen in early spring is common practice with most farmers. Hence the derivation of the T sum 100 or 200 which is an aggregate of temperature in degrees centigrade above zero. Towards the end of the winter, stocks of hay or silage run low and a delay in spring growth can be quite expensive if more conserved material has to be bought in. That is why early bite is important.

The organic farmer cannot use nitrogen but, interestingly, observations at Haughley research station in Suffolk on the closed organic system showed, over a period of twenty years, that with the exception of late cold springs, the organic pastures began to grow earlier than the conventional fields. It was also observed that the organic fields contained a higher proportion of humus, which increased the moisture retention of the soil making them less likely to flood, and thus less at risk of poaching by cattle.

Of the 18.5 million hectares of agricultural land in Great Britain in 1989, two thirds was grassland (31% rough grazing, 28% permanent grassland and 8% temporary grassland). The area covered by temporary grassland was 1.6 million hectares, an area almost the size of Wales, but an area that had declined by 15% since 1980.

Grass species and productivity

Grass breeding in the last 50 years has concentrated almost entirely on perennial ryegrass and more than 90% of the grass seed sown is perennial ryegrass; but it has been bred to respond to fertiliser nitrogen. The question the organic farmer has to answer is should he follow the fashion and use seed mixtures dominated by perennial ryegrass or should he consider meadow fescue, timothy, meadow foxtail and crested dogstail? He is interested both in the productivity of the ley and also in the effect the ley has on soil structure, the replenishment of the humus content and the fertility of the subsequent arable crops.

Sir George Stapledon considered that the legume, and in particular wild white clover, was the keystone of land improvement. What should the place of other legumes be, of red clover, lucerne and sainfoin? The mineral nutrition of grazing stock is of great importance and certain herbs contain a much higher proportions of calcium, phosphate and trace elements than perennial ryegrass. A greater diversity of plants from a wider range of species than the grasses and legumes will increase the dietary constituents of sheep and cattle. But which ones should be included? Is there a system of grazing management that can retain the valuable herbs in the pasture? They are expensive to include in a seeds mixture.

Permanent grassland, which can be subdivided into grassland over 5 years old (5.2 million ha) and rough grazing (5.9 million ha), covers 60% of the agricultural land of the United Kingdom. Within this huge area of the country there is a large difference in productivity, even without artificial nitrogen, ranging from the best 'fattening' pastures to the poorest nardus moorland. Grassland improvements have tended to be concentrated on the poorer upland pastures, using drainage, lime and basic slag, and the introduction of better grass species and clover. Permanent grassland has been characterised by Stapledon in ascending order of usefulness, nardus, molinia, fescue, agrostis and finally ryegrass pastures. His preferred solution, particularly for the middle order pastures, fescue and agrostis, was to plough them up and sow down a mixture of mainly ryegrass and white clover.

Assessing grass productivity

A central thesis of this book is that before permanent grassland, particularly, can be improved, an attempt must be made to assess its productivity. If a reasonably accurate table could be made, based on indicators such as summer rainfall, soil type, elevation, species and number of growing days, without involving the farmer in too many expensive analyses, then he would have a base line from which to work. A yield figure can be established on the fields that can be taken for hay or silage but it is the grazing fields, which are the majority, where the problem of yield definition exists. Only if an initial value for productivity is made can the extent of any husbandry improvements be measured.

Livestock units are one way of getting a feel for the productivity of a field, but there is the problem of keeping an annual record of the stock that have grazed a field, assessing whether they have gained or lost weight and how much milk they have produced. There is also the problem of whether management has fully utilised the grass. It is possible to graze 500 ewes on a 5 ha field for 7 days and record 700 grazing days per ha. It is doubtful whether these ewes will eat as much herbage as 50 ewes kept on the same field for 70 days.

Why is some grassland unproductive?

Writers such as Sutton and Stapledon were convinced that thousands of low-lying meadows and upland pastures were not yielding half the produce which could be obtained from them 'were the land in better heart'. The reasons stated for this deterioration were:

1. the practice of taking hay crops for several successive years without giving any adequate return of manure;
2. cutting the crops for hay very late in the season, and so exhausting the plant;
3. grazing animals on the land without feeding them an external supplement (cake, corn or hay from elsewhere);
4. overstocking and thus overgrazing;
5. the tolerance of too many weeds;
6. and finally a succession of wet summers which causes poorly drained pastures to become 'sour and unwholesome'.

It is unlikely that our grassland is much more productive now. But unless there is a method of estimating yield, change cannot be charted. A poor yield may be caused by adverse weather conditions, so a control or average needs to be established to disentangle the change in productivity caused by climate from that caused by management.

A great deal of advice on the improvement of permanent grassland is based on the presence of perennial ryegrass. If the field has plenty of ryegrass then it is assumed to be productive, if it has little or no ryegrass then the advice is to plough it up and resow with a seeds mixture containing predominantly ryegrass. There are two basic objections to this. First, it has been shown, from cut plots, that so-called weed grasses, such as crested dogstail, meadow foxtail and Yorkshire fog actually outyield perennial ryegrass, particularly under conditions with no added nitrogen. Second, unless the nutrition of the plants is improved, yield won't improve, no matter what species are present. It has been contended that a great proportion of the improvement in yield brought about by ploughing-up old grassland and resowing it with a temporary ley, was not because of the new seeds mixture but because of the release of the fertility that had been accumulating under the old pasture.

The organic farmer cannot use high levels of artificial fertiliser, particularly nitrogen, to boost his grassland yield and must rely on the use of compost, the right grass and legume species and proper grassland management. There is also a well-founded reluctance to plough up old pastures. A lot of work and thought goes into proper grassland management and it is vital that grassland productivity be assessed.

Organic grassland needs careful management; it is no use assuming that because it is organic everything will thrive. Nature is not that beneficent. If each field could be made into hay and the bales counted, the poorer fields would soon become obvious and improvement be sought.

The claim against artificial fast-acting fertilisers is, first, that they use too much support energy and are depleting valuable resources; second, that they make the soil hard and unworkable and, third, that they stimulate the plant and build up what Sir Albert Howard called "a bastard structure" made from inorganic nitrogen rather than from organic protein. Furthermore, sulphate of ammonia is actually used as a destroyer of earthworms. Howard stresses the usefulness of humus which, on decaying, releases carbonic acid, which in turn dissolves the minerals in the soil; when dissolved these can be assimilated. In a sense the reliance on slow acting fertilisers for organic farmers, such as rock phosphate and rock potash, may be creating false hope. It is possible that they are so slow acting that no phosphoric acid or potassium is ever released.

Newman Turner draws the distinction between phosphate being deficient, which he says is never the case, and being unavailable, or locked up. This is an important question for the organic grassland farmer. He can use lime and basic slag, which will supply phosphate. He can use compost and seaweed. But which should be used when, and how cost-effective are they? Their use needs authenticating, scientifically.

Another problem in grassland is weeds. When does a useful herb become a noxious weed? There are docks, thistles, couch, nettles, bracken, dandelions, daisies and there used to be coltsfoot. One way of looking at weeds is to try to turn them into useful plants. If they are deep rooting, bring up minerals and contain an above average amount of calcium or magnesium in their leaves, and if they are palatable, animals will graze them *in situ*, for no extra cost. The feeding of dandelions to dairy cows in Switzerland has been shown to increase milk yield. If they won't eat them in the pasture, they can be turned into hay (like nettles) or composted to make humus. But this argument should not be carried too far. Docks are protein rich, so they can be used, but not grown in preference to grass or clover.

There is no doubt that some herbs are weeds and they have to be controlled in pastures, if not eliminated altogether, without the use of herbicides. Basically they must be weakened by cultivation at the right time, before they spread, either vegetatively or by seed dispersal.

Grass suffers from rust, legumes are attacked by stem eelworm and Sitona weevils. How can the organic farmer protect his grassland? One theory is that he should use resistant varieties and that the use of insecticides and sprays has protected varieties that are genetically weak. Another view is that if sufficient organic manure and compost is used on the grassland so that their nutrition is satisfied, then disease incidence will be much reduced. This needs assessing scientifically. The third approach is that with the proper rotation and mixed farming using a wide range of species, minor pests will not become the plagues which are caused by monoculture. If pesticides, fungicides and herbicides are banned, then the existing fauna will keep each other in check. Remove one part of the food chain artificially and the natural order goes haywire.

Using organic grass efficiently

Considerable emphasis has been placed on assessing grassland productivity. However, it is no use painstakingly building up grassland fertility if it is then used inefficiently. For this the animal is all-important, because human food has not been manufactured directly from grass as yet. Efforts have been made, but without our own rumen or large caecum the process is very expensive. There are two aspects of grassland management that need consideration. First there is the effect of the animal on the sward, defoliation, treading, dunging and urinating. An overgrazed sward will deteriorate, so the stocking rate must not be too high, particularly during very wet weather in the winter and during summer drought. On the other hand undergrazing will cause herbage wastage, an increase in coarse indigestible clumps of senescing material and probably an increase in the less desirable species. Cattle, sheep, goats, pigs, poultry and possibly even horses, should be used to increase the proportion of the sward that is desirable, as well as maintaining soil fertility. But do we know how to do this - and which grass and herb species are desirable for which animal?

The second aspect is the effect of the sward on the animal. Animals eat more if the herbage is kept highly digestible, and the more they eat the more they produce. It is stated that animals will balance their own diet, provided they are offered a wide enough choice. If this is the case, why do they eat toxic plants? The theory sounds rather too convenient to be true.

Pastures can also be used for hay or silage. There has been a gradual swing from hay to silage, mainly because the making of silage is less weather-dependent and the prejudice against it as a feed for animals has been slowly overcome. As mentioned above a late first cut of hay, possibly to allow the spread of wild flowers in the meadow, is detrimental to the grass plant and the consuming animal, because digestibility falls rapidly with increasing maturity. There is no reason why the organic farmer should not make organic silage; it can be well made without sulphuric or formic acid or other undesirable additives.

The organic farmer should and will have fields containing a much higher proportion of legumes than his conventional neighbour, if only because he will be using no inorganic nitrogen fertiliser. Legumes can be conserved satisfactorily and will improve winter nutrition in the same way as they boost growth and milk yield during grazing.

The process of conversion from conventional to organic grassland can take several years. If the pastures have been receiving substantial amounts of artificial N, P and K, then productivity will be reduced and so will income. Furthermore if the legume status of the fields is low then the establishment of useful amounts of clover will take time and money, because legume seed is expensive. There has been talk of government support for organic farming during the conversion process in the UK. Now that the German government supports conversion to organic farming financially there has been a big increase in the German organic acreage. It is almost as if the government is waiting to see how much popular support there is for organic food before following the trend, instead of being bold enough to take a lead. There are grants for set-aside, which is land that is taken out of agricultural production altogether, except for grazing by horses. This is a negative approach, the likely consequence of which is to intensify production on the remaining land.

Organic farming will reduce output per ha, particularly of cereals and milk. It therefore fulfils the extensification objective of the Common Agricultural Policy for the EC countries. If it can also be demonstrated that organic farming has environmental, conservation and social benefits, then the case for financial support is strengthened. The amount of support money actually available may well depend on how far surpluses are reduced.

Three basic farming systems are examined in this book. One is the all-grass livestock farm which predominates in the north and west. This type of farm gradually merges into the upland farm with limited acreage for hay or silage (because of slope or rocks), farms which are mainly dependent on sheep and beef. The third type of farm is the arable farm with temporary grass as part of the rotational system. Sound organic principles will increase the length of the ley and decrease the number of consecutive years of cereal cropping. This will reduce the cereal acreage in this country, increase the area under temporary grass, reduce the use of artificial fertiliser and herbicides and increase the purity of the water in our rivers. Cereal production has been profitable, and has been subsidised, but there is over production of wheat and barley in Europe. Government support for the organic option, which will decrease the income of agrochemical firms and the 'barley barons', would be a courageous policy. And it would reduce the risk of soil erosion and water pollution.

What of the future of organic farming and food production? The desire is increasing for safer food and a farming system that takes more account of the way it is produced. The demand is consumer-led. Forecasts of the share of organic food vary between a conservative 10% to an optimistic 20% by the year 2000. But both these figures represent a large increase from the current base of less than 1% for organic milk and meat, which are the main products from organic grassland. To some extent the future of organic meat production is linked to the rise in the number of vegetarians. The case for being vegetarian is based on three arguments. First, that the number of people in the world who are starving is increasing, despite modern technology, and that crop production is more energy efficient than animal production. Second, that intensive livestock production has become distasteful if not actually cruel and, third, that meat is bad for you. People who are vegetarian for the second or possibly the third reason may well choose to eat organic meat, but it will still be animal flesh that they are consuming, however humanely reared and slaughtered.

References

Balfour, E.B. 1976 *The Living Soil and the Haughley Experiment.* Universe Books, New York, 383 pp.
Lampkin, N. 1991 *Organic Farming.* Farming Press, Ipswich, 701 pp.
Newman Turner. 1955 *Fertility Pastures.* Faber and Faber, London, 204 pp.
Stapledon, R.G. 1936 *The land now and tomorrow.* Faber and Faber, London, 336 pp.
Sutton, M.J., Sutton, M.H.F. and Percival, J. 1929 *Permanent and temporary pastures.* Ninth Edition. Simpkin Marshall Ltd., London, 202 pp.
Friend Sykes. 1951 *Food, Farming and the Future.* Faber and Faber, London, 294pp.

Chapter 2

Grasses

Does the organic farmer follow his conventional counterpart and rely mainly on perennial ryegrass for his temporary leys or should he consider other grasses? Indeed if he chooses crested dogstail is it still available at a reasonable price? In this chapter a number of possible grass species are described, with legumes and herbs forming the subject matter of subsequent chapters.

Historically there has been a considerable change in the composition of recommended seeds mixtures for temporary pastures, and this has affected both the varieties used and the number included.

Nearly a hundred years ago, Robert Elliot, the pioneer of the Clifton Park mixture advocated the following seeds mixture for the light land of his farm in the Cheviots (Table 2.1):

Table 2.1.   Improved Inner Kaimrig Mixture

	Seed (kg/ha)
Cocksfoot	12
Meadow fescue	6
Tall fescue	5
Tall oat-like grass	4
Hard fescue	1
Rough-stalked meadow grass	0.5
Smooth-stalked meadow grass	1
Golden oat grass	0.5
Italian ryegrass	4
White clover	2.5
Alsike clover	1
Late flowering red clover	2.5
Kidney vetch	2.5
Chicory	4
Burnet	10
Sheep's parsley	1
Yarrow	0.5
	57 kg/ha

This would be an expensive mixture today, but one that he found of great merit and one that attracted considerable public attention and use. There are four main points of interest. One, there is no perennial ryegrass. Two, there are 17 different species. Three, several species are present in small quantities and four, herbs are well represented (this will be discussed in a subsequent chapter).

Elliot held strong views about the relative merits of cocksfoot and perennial ryegrass. He regarded the preference for ryegrass as accidental and cites a letter from James Hunter, the founder of the well known agricultural seeds firm in Chester. The gist of the case is that up to 1882 all the leading seed merchants based their recommendations on a paper by Lawson in Agrostographics in 1834, in which he recommended the use of 12-30 lbs of perennial ryegrass per acre (about quarter to half of the whole seeding). But Hunter points out that ryegrass was almost the only grass seed that was easily obtained at that time and secondly that Lawson misquotes the famous Sinclair, who in reality recommended that the proportion of perennial ryegrass should only be about one in twenty. In short Robert Elliot, backed by Mr Faunce de Laune, were strongly anti-ryegrass and pro-cocksfoot: a campaign that has been renewed more recently by Snaydon (1987).

Ironically, the preface to Robert Elliot's book "The Clifton Park System of Farming", was written by Sir George Stapledon, who was more responsible than anyone for recommending that thousands of acres of permanent pasture should be sown down to perennial ryegrass and white clover and for ensuring that his own Welsh Plant Breeding Station should concentrate on improving perennial ryegrass almost to the exclusion of any other grass. In 1991 perennial ryegrass constituted over 90% of all grass seed sold.

The question remains. Is the almost total reliance on perennial ryegrass right for the organic farmer? Should plant breeding in Britain have neglected other grass species, remembering that agricultural science has been, and probably still is, often carried out more for the benefit of the scientist than for the farmer?

Dawson (1969) details several interesting points about the changes in seeds mixtures. Farmers used to buy individual components and mix them themselves but by 1968 only 12% of seed was supplied in farmers' own prescription, the remaining 88% were for advertised mixtures. These mixtures also changed. Cockle Park mixtures gradually gave way to what he termed "the present day sophisticated mixtures - simple mixtures compounded to produce grass for very specific methods of utilisation". These changes were intimately linked with a progressive increase in the amount of nitrogen applied. Little or no nitrogen was applied to the commercial Cockle Park mixture, but the simple ryegrass mixtures received up to 400 units of nitrogen per acre. This is a point of considerable significance for the organic farmer.

The basis of the simple mixture is first that if there is a best grass for a particular situation, e.g. silage making or grazing, then why dilute this grass with something inferior and reduce yield, and second that with only one cultivar, then heading date will be the same and cutting date can be geared to a preselected digestibility. Management has been simplified, but the question that should really have been addressed is: was this beneficial to the animal, not only for its milk yield, but also for its health, to eat one or, at best, two cultivars of only one grass species, namely perennial ryegrass, year in and year out?

The real problem that the plant breeders have in their work is finding a cheap method of evaluating new cultivars, if possible without the use of the animal, and also, as mentioned above, with insufficient knowledge of what farmers really want. The criteria that have been used for selecting promising new grass varieties are dry matter yield, digestibility, heading date, persistence and disease resistance, but mainly the first two, which can be combined into digestible organic matter yield. The animal is not required. Newman Turner would undoubtedly have added the health of the grazing animal and its reproductive performance. Elliot was very keen on the effect of the species on soil structure, hence his liking for cocksfoot and chicory. The suitability of the grass as a companion rather than a competitor with legumes and herbs is also important.

Unfortunately, the health of the grazing animal and its reproductive performance would require the use of a great many animals to test scientifically. And so it has remained a subjective opinion. But for the organic farmer mixed farming and mixed swards are a cornerstone of his philosophy, and the notion that animals benefit from being offered a wide range of plants and therefore of nutrients seems eminently reasonable. But it makes sward management more complex.

Types of temporary ley

As cereal growing is likely to be one of the most consistently profitable enterprises on arable farms, there is a strong temptation to keep the ley break as short as possible, or to do without it altogether. The composition of one or two year leys is different from four year leys. For the short ley what is wanted is fast establishment of the grass and clover, and for this purpose Italian or tetraploid perennial ryegrass plus red clover must form the basis (e.g. 22 kg tetraploid perennial ryegrass, 7 kg tetraploid red clover per ha).

The four year ley, however, will improve soil structure considerably and also, if the legume establishes well, make more nitrogen available to the subsequent crops. Recommendations for this longer ley will be detailed after the section on the individual grass species.

Small plot experiments, using cutting as the method of harvesting rather than the grazing animal, have been carried out to examine the dry matter production of a range of grass species (Table 2.2).

Table 2.2   Annual dry matter yield (kg per hectare) of grasses with no nitrogen, mean of 3 years.

Grass species	Cowling + Lockyer (1965)	Frame (1990)
Perennial ryegrass	1360	2380
Timothy	1460	1790
Meadow fescue	1040	
Cocksfoot	1400	
Agrostis tenuis	810	2630
Yorkshire fog	3680	
Red fescue	3280	
Smooth meadow grass	1490	
Crested dogstail	2560	
Sweet vernal	2570	

14

In each of the cited experiments the seedbed received a compound fertiliser and thereafter K_2O and P_2O_5 were given. Grasses were sown in individual plots and harvested with a mower, 4, 5 or 6 times per year, leaving a stubble of 3-4 cm. In the first experiment, timothy and cocksfoot had similar yields to perennial ryegrass. In the second experiment, agrostis, Yorkshire fog, red fescue, crested dogstail and sweet vernal all outyielded perennial ryegrass, though the digestibility of red fescue was significantly lower than that of perennial ryegrass.

These yields compare with 10-12 t DM/ha for ryegrass + 300-400 kg N/ha. Table 2.3 shows the yield of the same grasses in association with white clover. The total yield of each grass/clover combination was measured, and then separated into the portions of grass and clover.

Table 2.3.   **Annual yield (dry matter, kg/ha, mean of 3 years) of each grass + white clover mixture.**

Grass species	Cowling + Lockyer (1965)			Frame (1990)		
	Grass	Clover	Total	Grass	Clover	Total
Perennial ryegrass	2419 + 3150 (56%)		= 5569	5721 + 2766 (31%)		= 8487
Timothy	2847 + 2522 (47%)		= 5369			
Meadow fescue	2298 + 2937 (56%)		= 5235			
Cocksfoot	3060 + 2500 (45%)		= 5560			
Agrostis	1700 + 3542 (68%)		= 5242	3400 + 1850 (35%)		= 5250
Red fescue				5550 + 3700 (40%)		= 9250
Crested dogstail				3863 + 4443 (53%)		= 8306
Smooth meadow grass				4314 + 4036 (48%)		= 8350
Yorkshire fog				5626 + 2550 (35%)		= 8276
Rough meadow grass*				3770 + 4960 (57%)		= 8730

* 1 year's result only

Cowling and Lockyer make the point that the variability in yield of grass has been compensated by the yield of clover, thus making a herbage total that only varies from 5.2 to 5.6 t DM per ha. This is most apparent in the comparison between the highest yielding grass, cocksfoot (3.1) + clover (2.5) and the lowest yielding grass, agrostis (1.7) + clover (3.5). With the exception of the agrostis plots in Frame's experiment, the same point is evident.

In Cowling and Lockyer's experiment, clover yield, and its proportion in the mixture varied markedly between years. The overall yield of herbage was considerably higher in Frame's experiment. In both experiments clover yields were much higher than those normally associated with grazing experiments, ranging from 45 to 68% in the first experiment and from 31 to 57% in the second. Considering a companion grass for clover in the first experiment amongst the more usually sown grasses, then only meadow fescue has as high a clover proportion as perennial ryegrass (52%). In the second experiment, the secondary grasses, crested dogstail, and rough and smooth meadow grass all favoured white clover.

The testing of grasses by animals has received less attention, mainly because of cost. This is unfortunate, because the grasses have to be utilised by the animal even though some experiments on converting grass into textured protein for direct human consumption have shown promise. Cattle and sheep differ in their preference for white clover, and also in their manner of grazing. It is quite possible therefore that a grass that enhances milk production in cattle may not be the most suitable for fattening lambs. The significance of this is that digestibility may not be the only criterion governing intake and performance.

In a comparison between cocksfoot and perennial ryegrass, Greenhalgh and Reid (1969), found that the ryegrass was 4-5 percentage units more digestible than cocksfoot and generally contained more soluble carbohydrate. But intake and milk yield in the spring were much the same. Only in the summer was milk yield significantly higher for the dairy cows grazing the ryegrass. The cocksfoot sward was described as more open, allowing the ingress of Poa annua.

A three-year experiment in Ireland (Moloney and Murphy, 1965), compared the effect of sward type on the liveweight gain of yearling sheep. No fertiliser nitrogen was used in the experiment. The results are shown in Table 2.4.

Table 2.4. The influence of sward type on the liveweight gain of yearling sheep (kg/ha, mean of 3 years).

Sward type	Mean
Perennial ryegrass	562
Meadow foxtail	662
Rough-stalked meadow grass	631
Yorkshire fog	600
Red fescue	404

These results make a strong case for the use of secondary grasses in temporary leys. They also indicate forcefully, as does other work, that because permanent pasture contains little or no perennial ryegrass, it should not be ploughed up because it is thought to be less productive.

Grasses are required for a variety of purposes and it is unrealistic to assume that one grass will answer all purposes. Grasses are required for a) earliness b) lateness c) winter hardiness d) longevity e) disease resistance f) grazing g) conservation h) dry soils i) wet soils j) to improve soil structure k) upland conditions l) poor soils and m) compatibility with legumes and herbs.

Grass Species

If an organic farmer is to decide on the most suitable seeds mixture for his own farm, rather than following a standard seedsman's formula, then he must have knowledge of the capabilities of each grass species. There are sixteen possible species to consider:

Perennial Ryegrass *(Lolium perenne)*

The mainstay of most seed mixtures now, and for the last 20 years. There are many cultivars, both diploid and tetraploid, so that suitable types or varieties can be chosen for earliness, mid-season, lateness, conservation or grazing. The more upright tetraploid has been shown to be more compatible with white clover than the less erect, more densely tillering diploid, such as S23 or Melle. Ryegrass is a favourite with seedsmen because it sets seeds easily, and with plant breeders. Seed is cheap. The grass is aggressive, is easily mismanaged, but withstands treading.

From what has been said in earlier sections, it is not the highest yielding grass in the no-nitrogen organic situation, there are certainly doubts whether it is the grazing animal's first choice, and it is not drought resistant. It has also been reported that the cutting varieties of perennial ryegrass are not persistent, and the grazing varieties are not easy to cut.

Italian ryegrass *(Lolium multiflorum)*

Undoubtedly the first choice for the short ley. Establishes quickly. IRG needs warmth and moisture and in rich damp soils the growth is rapid. Not tested in zero-nitrogen trials. May not be satisfactory on poor clay soils.

Cocksfoot *(Dactylis glomerata)*

The foundation of the Clifton Park mixture of Robert Elliot. High yielding, deep rooting, very suitable for dry areas and thin soils. Excellent for improving soil structure. Seed is relatively cheap. Thrives under trees (American name is Orchard grass). Useful for foggage.

Aggressive towards white clover; needs careful management to prevent it forming senescent clumps.

Timothy *(Phleum pratense)*

A late flowering grass which is winter hardy and forms the basis of pastures in the colder regions of Europe. Blends well with white clover, possibly because of its later growth. Well suited to damp areas and clay districts. Easy to cut and is very persistent under cutting management. Seed is relatively cheap. Combines well with the earlier growing meadow fescue. Relatively high yielding. Formed the basis, with ryegrass and cocksfoot, of Gilchrist's Cockle Park mixture.

Meadow foxtail *(Alopecurus pratensis)*

An early, high yielding grass, supporting excellent animal performance in no N trials and forming the basis of early seeds mixtures. Persistent and makes a good aftermath. Endures spring frosts and cold well. Quite clearly an excellent grass but the seed is extremely expensive (more than ten times as expensive as perennial ryegrass).

Crested dogstail *(Cynosurus cristatus)*

Another grass that was more widely used in seeds mixtures a hundred years ago. A valuable grazing grass that has been shown to outyield perennial ryegrass in 0 nitrogen experiments and makes one of the best companion grasses for white clover. Not a particularly expensive seed.

Meadow fescue *(Festuca pratensis)*

The grass that is always recommended with white clover and one that is still featured in the NIAB list of grasses and legumes. Resistant to winter cold and flourishing in low lying meadows with strong, deep soil. Much liked by animals. Seed is cheap.

Tall fescue *(Festuca elatior)*

When farmers ask for an early grass, with a long growing season the grass that is always recommended is tall fescue. It is also high yielding and drought resistant, but unfortunately animals don't seem to like it. Seed is reasonably cheap.

Red fescue *(Festuca rubra)*

A fine-leaved grass that has been shown in recent trials to be high yielding. Well suited to poor upland soils. Hard wearing. A pasture grass and not a hay grass. Seed is cheap.

Rough-stalked meadow grass *(Poa trivialis)*

Relatively high yielding and a good companion for white clover. Does well on strong moist soils. Not very winter hardy and unsuited to dry land. Regarded by some as a weed grass to be eradicated. Seed is reasonably cheap.

Smooth-stalked meadow grass *(Poa pratensis)*

Popular in America where it is known as Kentucky Blue grass. It is usually preferred to rough-stalked, particularly on drier soils. An early pasture grass, it is also useful for forage. Seed is cheap. Shown to be as high yielding as perennial ryegrass and a good companion grass for white clover.

Common bent *(Agrostis tenuis)*

Not a grass that has featured in seeds mixtures, even though it is very common in the better soils of hill pastures. Not particularly high yielding but not aggressive towards white clover.

Yorkshire fog *(Holcus lanatus)*

An interesting grass that has been shown to be high yielding in cutting trials with no nitrogen and to have supported better liveweight gain by sheep than perennial ryegrass. This suggests that its normal categorisation as a weed grass is unjust. Not a good companion for white clover, and seed is expensive.

Sweet vernal grass *(Anthoxanthum odoratum)*

Contains coumarin and imparts a pleasant odour to the hay crop. Can yield quite highly when grown alone, but is normally found as a constituent of meadows and upland pastures.

Forage bromes *(Bromus wildenowii)*

Useful as a cutting grass on dry soils, relatively digestible and palatable.

18

References

Cowling, D.W. and Lockyer, D. 1965 *A comparison of the reaction of different grass species to fertilizer nitrogen and to growth in association with white clover.* 1 Yield of dry matter. Journal of the British Grassland Society 20, 197-204.

Dawson, J.L. 1969 *Grass and Forage Breeding. in: Herbage Varieties in Northern Britain, Occasional Symposium* No. 5. British Grassland Society 103-109.

Elliot, R. 1908 *The Clifton Park System of Farming.* 4th Edition. Simpkin Marshall Ltd, London.

Frame, J. 1990 *Herbage productivity of a range of grass species in association with white clover.* Grass and Forage Science, 57-64.

Greenhalgh, J.F.D. and Reid, G.W. 1969 *The herbage consumption and milk production of cows grazing S24 ryegrass and S37 cocksfoot.* Journal of the British Grassland Society, 24, 98-103.

Moloney, D. and Murphy, W.E. 1963-5 *Research Reports, Soils Division, An Foras Taluntais,* pp. 68-90.

Snaydon, R. 1987 *The Botanical Composition of Pastures. in: Managed Grasslands,* B. Analytical Studies (Ed. Snaydon, R.W.) Elsevier, Amsterdam.

PERENNIAL RYE GRASS
(*Lolium perenne* L.).

ITALIAN RYE GRASS

(*Lolium multiflorum* Lam. = *L. italicum* Braun.

COCKSFOOT ; ORCHARD GRASS
(*Dactylis glomerata* L.).

22

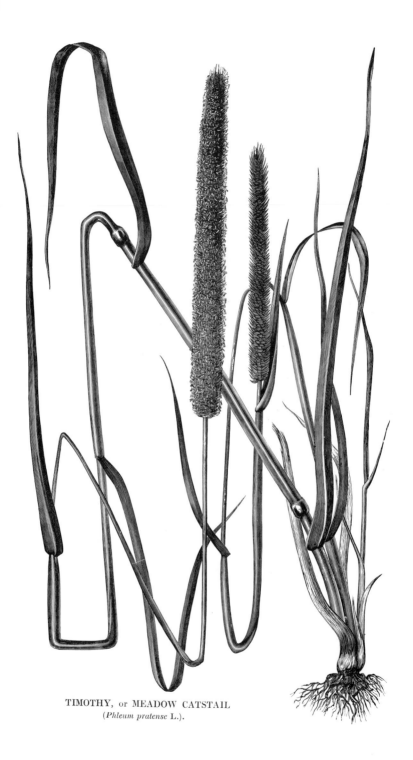

TIMOTHY, or MEADOW CATSTAIL
(*Phleum pratense* L.).

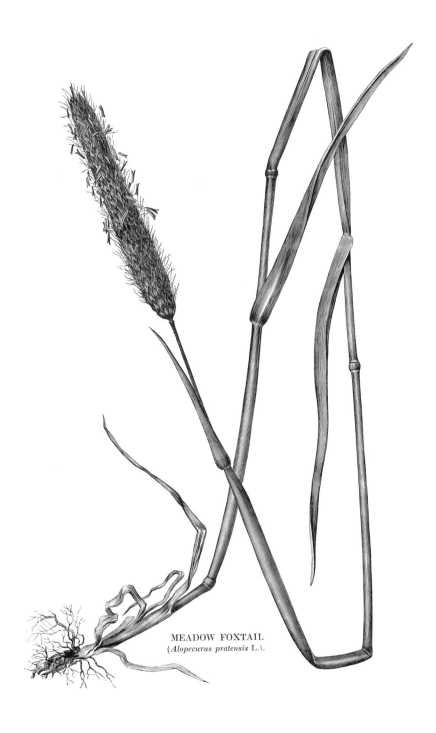

MEADOW FOXTAIL
(*Alopecurus pratensis* L.).

CRESTED DOGSTAIL
(*Cynosurus cristatus* L.).

MEADOW FESCUE
(*Festuca pratensis* Huds.).

TALL FESCUE
(*Festuca elatior* L.).

ROUGH-STALKED MEADOW GRASS,
or ORCHESTON GRASS
(*Poa trivialis* L.).

28

SMOOTH-STALKED MEADOW GRASS; KENTUCKY BLUE GRASS;
JUNE GRASS (*Poa pratensis* L.).

SWEET-SCENTED
VERNAL
(*Anthoxanthum odoratum* L.).

 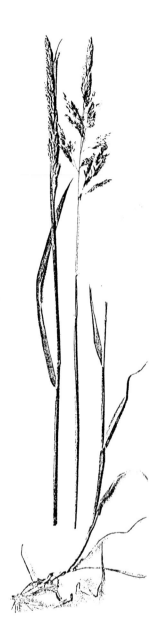

CREEPING FESCUE or RED FESCUE
(Festuca rubra L. subspecies rubra.)

YORKSHIRE FOG
(Holcus lanatus L.)

Chapter 3

Legumes

Legumes are unique in that they can fix atmospheric nitrogen. This is done by symbiotic Rhizobia bacteria which form nodules on the roots of legumes and use carbon compounds from the host plant as an energy source to fix nitrogen from the air. Most white clover plants in lowland soils produce nodules after infection by indigenous strains of *Rhizobium trifolii*. It is only clover seed destined to be sown in deep peats and other hill soil types that need inoculation and lucerne.

Legumes can utilise nitrogen from two sources: from the atmosphere and from soil mineral nitrogen. If plenty of soil mineral N is available then the legume will use this nitrogen and not rely so heavily on fixing soil atmospheric N. This is why the correlation between the amount of clover present in the sward and the amount of nitrogen fixed is so variable.

Factors making soil mineral N less available are an increase in soil carbon content (or C/N ratio). Relatively more mineral N is immobilised during microbial breakdown of soil organic matter, leaving less N available to the plant or a reduced rate of mineralisation of N in the autumn and winter, caused by falling soil temperatures. In the same way on impoverished soils with low levels of mineral N, clover will have to compete with the associated grass species for the small amount of available mineral N and will therefore have to rely more on fixing atmospheric N. For the above reasons the level of N fixation per ha is not a good indicator of the amount of legume present.

Estimates for the amount of nitrogen fixed per ha by clover vary considerably, with 163 to 184 kg of N per ha per annum being the most commonly agreed, but the range is 86 to 392 kg N/ha, with the amount varying with the season. These values indicate the considerable ability of the legume to bring crucial nitrogen into the nutrient cycle, which is particularly important for the organic farmer.

The question of when this legume-fixed nitrogen becomes available to the grasses in the sward is of great importance, but is much less understood and controlled. The most likely period of release is in the year following its fixation. This is why short term experiments are unable to show an advantage in terms of grass production when in association with high levels of legume.

Red Clover *(Trifolium pratense)*

Red clover cultivars can be grouped into three main types, 'broad red' (double-cut, early flowering), 'single cut' (intermediate-flowering) and 'late flowering'. The early flowering types are biennial, erect, will give two cuts a year, and are less well-adapted to grazing than the late-flowering types. The late-flowering types are short-lived perennials (3 to 4 years), more prostrate in habit, and thus can withstand grazing. There are also 'wild' types that are smaller and strongly perennial.

Red clover, like lucerne, and unlike white clover, possesses a well-marked crown and does not spread. Hence, when the plant dies it leaves an empty space, and although the surrounding plants can compensate for this by increased aerial growth, there is a limit to this and the stand thins out. Red clover, again like lucerne, has a well-developed tap-root system which may penetrate the soil to a great depth.

Red clover is less tolerant of acid soil conditions than white clover, and grows best at pH 6.0 to 7.5. Doubt has been cast on the winter hardiness of red clover, but low temperature is not a limiting factor for red clover in Britain.

Red clover is sown in mixtures with other species as a major constituent in short term leys, particularly with Italian ryegrass for 1 to 2 year leys. Its great value, compared with white clover, is that it establishes quickly and is productive in its first year. Seed rates of red clover should be high; for instance a short term ley would consist, typically, of 10 kg Italian, and 10 kg red clover per ha.

Red clover can also be used in the more complex seeds mixtures for the longer 3 to 4 year leys. If the shorter-lived broad red clover is used (at 4 kg per ha) then it will establish early and then gradually die out to be replaced by the longer lasting, but slower establishing, white clover.

Yields of pure stands of red clover, grown for silage or hay, can reach 11 t DM per ha; more than white clover, but less than lucerne, but in a mixture with grass, yield is more likely to be 6 t per ha. Measured values for nitrogen fixation range from 103 to 249 kg per N per ha, with an average of 160 kg N/ha.

The chemical composition of red clover shows that it contains less cell wall constituents (cellulose and hemi-cellulose) than grass, thus promoting higher intake. Red clover is higher in protein and contains three times as much calcium as grass. There is more iron and cobalt in red clover than in grass but it is lower in manganese, selenium and silica. The magnesium content of red clover is higher than in grass, and also higher than in white clover, lucerne or sainfoin.

Improved animal performance on red clover has generally been accompanied by higher herbage intake compared with grass. With well-made red clover silage of similar digestibility to grass silage, increased milk yields of 10 to 13% have been found with red clover, and increased liveweight gains in beef cattle and lambs of 20 to 30%. Red clover, unlike white clover, contains more stem as it matures, so that when cut, in the mature stage, digestibility will be reduced.

Red clover has a high yield of protein-rich feed, which promotes better animal performance than grass; it fixes nitrogen and the seed is cheap. Why then does the amount of red clover sown annually fall so persistently?

The reasons are threefold, disease, bloat and oestrogens. Red clover populations and yields are greatly reduced by stem eelworm *(Ditylenchus dipsaci)*, and clover rot *(Sclerotinia trifoliorum)* and stem eelworm are endemic in a great many soils in Britain. It may be necessary to abstain from growing stem eelworm host plants for 8 years in heavy soils and 2 years in light soils. Clover rot is both seed and soil-borne and where rot is prevalent a break of 8 to 12 years is advisable. Certain varieties are resistant to clover rot, but less to eelworm.

Bloat is clearly a problem with grazing red clover, particularly with cattle, but can be overcome by introducing red clover into the diet gradually.

The oestrogens in red clover can cause a significant fall in the number of live lambs born to sheep if grazing is managed incorrectly. Red clover can be grazed safely at any time of the year except during the period of mating. If, for the two weeks before ram inclusion and for the duration of mating, the flock is kept off red clover, then there will be no problem.

The oestrogen in red clover that affects sheep is rendered harmless by the different metabolic pathways in cattle.

Summary

Red clover is a very useful nitrogen-fixing legume, valuable as a green manure. It establishes fast in short term leys and enhances animal performance. Its proneness to disease and the threat of bloat and oestrogenic disorder can be countered through knowledge and appropriate management.

White clover *(Trifolium repens)*

Types

Three main types of white clover are recognised. Small-leaved, wild white types, with short petioles and dense, many-branched stolons forming roots at most nodes; intermediate-leaf sized white clovers, such as S100 and Huia, and finally the large-leafed varieties, such as Blanca and Aran, which are more upright, higher yielding under cutting, with shorter less branched stolons, large leaflets and long petioles. Generally speaking, the small-leaved types live longer, but all white clover types are true perennials.

Growth habit

In white clover the primary stem is short and its growth limited. The lower axillary buds on this stem develop into stolons which spread over the soil surface. The primary root is a tap-root, but its activity soon diminishes and it has usually died within 18 months. Adventitious roots are produced at the nodes, and these enable the new shoots to become independent units. Most of these roots are confined to the top 15 cm layer of the soil. White clover, unlike red clover and lucerne, is essentially a shallow-rooted plant. Some nodules occur on the young tap root but most are carried on the fine secondary roots.

As a group, the legumes germinate and emerge from the soil in a shorter period than the grasses, but their early post-emergence development is slower. This is an important factor when considering the successful introduction of white clover into permanent pasture by slot-seeding.

The natural geographic distribution of Rhizobium spp. usually corresponds with that of their legume hosts. For this reason it can be safely assumed that British soils contain the appropriate Rhizobium strain for white clover, without the need for seed inoculation. However, in the absence of a legume host, their numbers decline until such time as a legume is introduced. Less than 100 bacteria in the rhizosphere are sufficient to initiate infection, but once the first nodule is formed, progressively more bacteria are required for the formation of succeeding nodules.

Soil condition and temperature

Wild white clover tolerates more acid conditions than the other legumes, with an optimum range of pH 5.6 to 7.0. When white clover is sown with companion grasses, the amount of clover is drastically reduced by applying nitrogen. There appear to be few climatic factors that limit the distribution of white clover in Britain, although some cultivars may be badly checked by a mild early spring which encourages early growth, followed by cold conditions later. The optimal temperature for growth lies between 17 and 23°C.

Place in leys and permanent pasture

White clover is particularly important in permanent pasture, because of its perenniality, but it is also of considerable value in leys of 3 years or longer duration.

The type of white clover to sow depends on the system. In a 3 to 4 year ley, used mainly for conservation and beef and dairy cattle grazing, then the medium and large-leaved varieties are better because they are higher-yielding. Huia is the most commonly sown variety, possibly because it is cheapest, but Menna, Donna, Blanca and Alice are all good varieties.

There is considerable variation in the quantity of white clover to be sown as part of a new seeds mixture, but bearing in mind the importance of white clover for subsequent fertility, it is better to err on the generous side, despite the extra initial cost; thus 4 kg of white clover per ha makes sense, with 10 kg of companion grass, and 4 kg of red clover, for good legume cover in the first 2 years of the ley.

The least aggressive conventional grasses to be sown with white clover are meadow fescue, timothy, perennial ryegrass and cocksfoot, in that order. Recent research has shown that the more upright perennial ryegrasses, the tetraploids, make better companions for white clover than the diploids, mainly because they tiller less.

Referring back to table 2.3 for the organic farmer who is going to use no nitrogen, and who wants a companion grass for white clover, then consideration should be given to the use of crested dogstail and/or smooth meadow grass and red fescue. But the inclusion of more species means that management becomes increasingly complicated, particularly if components of the mixture are not to be swamped or grazed out.

The use of white clover in permanent pasture will be discussed more fully in a later chapter. The most suitable variety for permanent pasture and for sustained set stocking by sheep is wild white clover (S184) or Kent wild white. This small-leaved variety is the most resistant to close grazing by sheep, mainly because of its ability to send out stolons at ground level.

If sheep are to be grazed on the 3 to 4 year ley mentioned earlier, using medium or large leaved white clover, then a rotational system rather than set stocking or continuous grazing will give more clover in the leys and better sheep performance.

Seeds mixtures containing white clover can be undersown under spring barley in March, or direct-drilled in June or July. Direct-drilling is more reliable, providing the seedbed is moist, but will mean a longer period of fallow.

Yield and N fixation

White clover is not normally grown alone but yields of 6-8 t DM per ha have been recorded. Grown with grass, yields of 2.5 to 4.5 t DM per ha should be possible. Yield of grass plus white clover range from 5 to 8 t DM per ha. White clover becomes productive later in spring than the majority of grasses, contributing little until early May - but this date varies with altitude and latitude. In a mixture, it often yields more after the middle of July than before.

An average annual value for nitrogen fixation is 180 kg per ha (range 86 to 390), but as discussed above the value is dependent on mineral N availability, temperature, rainfall and amount of clover present.

Chemical composition

Owing to its persistent leafiness throughout the season, and the low ratio of stem to leaf harvested, white clover is lower in cellulose and lignin and higher in available carbohydrate, N, P and sulphur than the other forage legume species. It is also higher in sodium, chlorine and molybdenum. The digestibility of white clover remains high throughout the year and its protein content is also high.

Animal performance

White clover promotes better animal performance than ryegrass of similar digestibility, mainly because animals eat more. Experiments have shown a 15% increase in the milk yield of dairy cows and 25 to 30% increase in the liveweight gain of beef cattle and sheep. The increase in performance of animals offered grass/white clover at pasture will depend on the amount of clover present and the grazing system employed.

Disease and bloat

The main problems with white clover are clover rot *(Sclerotinia trifolium)*, slug damage and Sitona weevil. Resistance to clover rot is linked to variety.
   Precautions against bloat with cattle are the same as for red clover. There is no problem with sheep.
   White clover has been shown to be oestrogenic, but only when the leaves are diseased. The oestrogenic compound is not the same as that found in red clover or lucerne, and does not affect reproductive performance.

Summary

1. White clover is the most important legume for organic farmers because it is a) a perennial b) useful in mixtures c) promotes excellent animal performance d) can be grown on a wider range of soil pH.
2. It is not as disease prevalent as red clover and lucerne.
3. It needs careful management in long term leys, and makes very little contribution to short term leys because it is slow to establish.

Lucerne *(Medicago sativa)*

Types

Lucerne has been used as a fodder crop since 480 BC, but did not reach England until 1630. It differs from the clovers in that no distinctive locally-adapted cultivars have arisen in Britain, probably because of its failure to evolve an efficient pollination mechanism in the colder British climate. The best-adapted type of lucerne for Britain (Flamande) originated from an area in northern France, where the climate is similar.

Growth habit

Lucerne is an erect perennial, with its meristematic apex well above ground level. As the stems grow they become woody at the base. A crown of tissue develops at ground level from which buds develop to give 3 or 4 successive crops per season. Grazing in the first year of growth can be detrimental, but later growth can be grazed without damage to the meristematic region in the crown.

The root system consists of a short tap-root which may have a few large lateral roots. On most soils the tap root is 60 to 90 cm long, but in deep, well-drained soils, the tap root has been recorded at a depth of 7 m.

Soil and temperature conditions

Lucerne grows mainly in regions where the annual rainfall is less than 750 mm (29.5 ins) and only occasionally where it exceeds 1000 mm (39 ins). The optimum pH soil range is 6.2 to 7.8, and it rarely grows above altitude 300 m.

For these reasons it is mainly grown on calcareous soils in the East and South East of England, with 49% being grown in the Eastern Region, 17% in the South East and 13% in the East Midlands.

Place in the ley

The value of lucerne to those organic farmers on suitable soils is that it is the most high yielding of the legumes, and is more suited to conservation as hay, silage or for drying.

It is normally grown as a 3 or 4 year ley with a companion grass, normally meadow fescue or timothy. The reason for growing it with a companion grass is that the grass will compete with the weeds which tend to invade a pure stand of lucerne, particularly during the dormant winter phase. Hay and silage are more easily made with grass plus lucerne than with lucerne alone, the problem being its high buffering capacity (a measure of the resistance to lowering in pH of the crop) and low sugar content.

Lucerne should be undersown and not direct drilled, which will result in a weed problem. It is best undersown in spring wheat, rather than spring barley, as the lucerne is the major priority. The seed rate is 13 to 18 kg/ha plus 2.5 kg/ha of timothy or meadow fescue. Seed should be inoculated with nodulating bacteria.

Yield

A healthy lucerne crop gives consistent yields from year to year because of its virtual immunity to dry weather. Yields can be 10-14 t DM per annum. The highest cut is usually the first, but more than half of the total yield is harvested later in the season. Successful management involves infrequent cutting (3 cuts/year) or the equivalent amount of grazing (mob stocking for short periods, not continuous grazing). Persistence is greatly affected by management in the autumn, at which time it is important to maintain a high level of carbohydrate reserves in the roots by allowing good recovery growth immediately prior to the last grazing, and delaying the time of this grazing until growth has virtually ceased. Nitrogen fixation with lucerne averages about 300 kg per ha per annum.

Chemical composition

Like red and white clover, lucerne is low in cellulose and hemicellulose and high in protein, pectin and organic acids, principally succinic, malic and malonic acids. It contains more carotene, vitamin B, calcium, magnesium, iron and cobalt than grasses, but less manganese, selenium and silica.

Animal performance

Animals eat more lucerne than grass of a similar digestibility and perform better in consequence, but the results from production experiments with cattle and sheep offered lucerne do not show such a marked advantage over grass as with white clover. The advantage will be in production per unit area because of the high yield of lucerne compared with grass with no nitrogen.

Diseases

Lucerne is particularly susceptible to verticillium wilt (*Verticillium albo-atrum*), and stem eelworm (*Ditylenchus dipsani*). It can also be affected by clover rot (*Sclerotinia trifolium*) and crown wart disease.

Varieties such as Vertus show good resistance to Verticillium wilt and to stem eelworm, whilst Vela is resistant to wilt only. To reduce the risk of infection, fields should be rested for 4 years between lucerne crops. During these four years the field should be kept clear of all dicotyledonous plants, as far as humanly possible. Wilt is frequently introduced with seed, so it is essential to use only healthy and efficiently-cleaned seed.

Cattle grazing lucerne can bloat, so the normal precautions should be taken.

Lucerne is oestrogenic but only when the leaves are infected. If eaten by sheep during the period of mating, the oestrogen can reduce reproductive performance, but the type of oestrogen in lucerne (coumestrol) is not as harmful as the one in red clover.

Summary

In the drier parts of the country, particularly on chalk and limestone, lucerne is a very high yielding, nutritious, nitrogen fixer. Excellent in drought conditions. Care should be taken about wilt and bloat.

Sainfoin (Onobrychis viciifolia)

Types

Sainfoin has been cultivated in Britain for over two hundred years. There are two main groups: Common and Giant, a division similar to that of the late-flowering and broad-red types in red clover. Giant, or Double-cut, is an early rapid-growing kind which gives heavy crops during one or two years. Common is later and continues to give good crops for five years or more. However, leys of 20 years old have been recorded. The lack of persistence of Giant is considered to be due to the greater tendency of the stems to flower, resulting in the presence of fewer leaves at soil level, and the destruction of a high proportion of the top growth at each cut. Frequent close cutting

38

decreases yield and eventually results in death. This would not occur in Common Sainfoin, which has a winter requirement for flowering, and produces rosettes but no stems after the first cut.

Growth habit

Sainfoin has numerous erect stems, and leaves borne on long petioles. The root system consists of a stout tap root with a few main branches. Sainfoin may multiply vegetatively by means of the short, brown, more or less ascending underground stems from old plants.

Soil type and distribution

Sainfoin has very similar soil requirements to lucerne, pH 6.0 to 7.5, which means that it seems confined naturally to the chalk and limestone areas of south, south-east and south-central England. It is not winter-hardy north of the Humber and is not found above altitudes of 300 m.

Place in rotation

The sowing of Sainfoin alone is expensive and rather precarious. When combined with strong-growing grasses there is less risk of failure, and the grasses keep down weeds and prevent the growth of couch and other weeds which almost invariably overrun a pure sainfoin ley, but the grasses will reduce the output of sainfoin. Like lucerne, the companion grasses most suitable are meadow fescue and timothy. The seed rate is very high, 62 kg per ha, which makes it very expensive.

Yield

Data on yield are scanty, but a good yield is 9 t of dry matter per annum.

Chemical composition

Little is known of the chemical composition, but it appears to contain about half as much calcium as the earlier mentioned legumes and to be low in sodium.

Animal performance

Direct measurements of voluntary intake have shown that more sainfoin is eaten than lucerne or red clover, and that it has given better growth in weaned lambs than any other legume tested, including white clover.

Diseases

There is no bloat problem with sainfoin. The disease problem is not well documented but sainfoin has been found to suffer from clover rot (*Sclerotinia trifolium*) and from tomato bushy stunt virus.

Summary

Sainfoin is a top quality legume for animal production, but the seed rate makes it expensive to sow and it is hard to keep weed-free. Bloat is not a problem.

Other Legumes

Writing 20 years ago, in 1972, Spedding and Diekmahns described the state of scientific knowledge about the other legumes, kidney vetch, trefoil, sweet clover and others, as scanty. They list their various disadvantages: for instance, lupins, common vetch and alsike clover may cause bloat; sweet clover is difficult to eradicate; kidney vetch and suckling clover give only low yields and the seeds of birdsfoot trefoil and common vetch are difficult to produce. However, they stress that when more knowledge is available, they could have a valuable part to play in certain agricultural situations. And it is the expert organic grassland farmer, such as Newman Turner, who is most likely to pioneer one of these less well known legumes. He asked a great many of the basic questions, about yield and animal preference with his dairy cows, back in 1950. His questions are still waiting to be answered. What constitutes a "balanced" sward for instance? It shouldn't only be perennial ryegrass and a bit of white clover, because the seed just happens to be available. A cheaper seeds mixture is only cheaper in productive terms if the resulting mixture promotes as good an animal performance. Listed below is the sum of knowledge on these lesser-used legumes.

Kidney Vetch *(Anthyllis vulneraria)*

A tufted deep-rooted legume occurring in stony places and dry pastures on calcareous soils. Described as withstanding prolonged drought and therefore of great service in temporary as well as permanent pastures on dry soils. Elliot found this on his gravelly soils at Clifton park, in the Scottish Borders; kidney vetch saved his livestock enterprise in the severe drought in 1899 as well as benefiting subsequent grass crops by its immense rootage, covered with nitrogen-collecting nodules.

Kidney vetch is either sown alone or under a cover crop of barley or oats. Some authors consider that it is unlikely to last for more than three seasons.

Lotus *(Lotus corniculatus)*

Also known as Birdsfoot trefoil. Lotus is a perennial with a well-developed tap-root. It is distributed extensively in Britain, being present in widely differing habitats, including both wet and dry situations. It can grow on land too poor, too shallow, too impermeable, too deficient in lime, too alkaline or too 'sick' to support red clover or lucerne. It is generally non-aggressive and is easily crowded out in mixtures.

In continental Europe high yields comparable with lucerne are obtained, but little experimental work has been conducted to determine its potential in Britain. The continental forms are more erect than the indigenous British ones, which tend to be prostrate and more suitable for grazing.

Lotus can be grazed without fear of bloat.

Lupin *(Lupinus angustifolius + L. lutens)*

There are blue lupins and yellow lupins. The most commonly grown species in Britain is blue lupin. Useful on poor, light land, especially if deficient in lime. Lupins are usually grazed by sheep, although there is damage of poisoning from certain varieties. Two distinct diseases are produced in sheep and cattle. The alkaloids of "bitter" lupins occur in high concentrations, especially in the seeds, and can induce a fatal paralysis of the respiratory and vasomotor centres. A totally different disease is "lupinosis" which is primarily caused by hepatotoxic substances produced by fungi that grow specifically on the dry mature vegetative parts of lupins following humid, rainy weather in summer. The green living plant is not toxic.

Trefoil *(Medicago lupulina)*

Also known as black medick (from the black seed pods) and hop clover. A fibrous-rooted annual, or at most a biennial. Not useful for cutting because of its procumbent growth habit. Seed is freely shed so that it can be regarded as virtually permanent.

It grows freely on almost any soil, preferring clay marl or a calcareous soil. Rarely sown alone, but frequently with white clover, or with meadow foxtail, sweet vernal and smooth-stalked meadow grass. It adds 'bottom' to pastures.

American sweet clover *(Melilotus alba)*

A highly productive legume which is very useful for improving poor soils, widely grown in America. It produces a great bulk of green manure and a tremendous rooting system. Can be used in a three-year rotation following corn and wheat.

Newman Turner found that his dairy cows did not like sweet clover, which is slightly bitter and unpalatable. He recommended that it be sown with cocksfoot, timothy or meadow fescue, as a major companion crop for silage purposes.

Alsike clover *(Trifolium lybridum)*

The name is derived from Syke in Sweden, from where it was introduced into Britain in the early 19th Century. It is a true perennial of upright habit like red clover. Were it not for the surface growth, and the consequent inability to withstand drought, Alsike would take a more important position. The plant is peculiarly adapted to damp soils, endures heat and cold well, succeeds in undrained clays. It flowers at the same time as late flowering red clover. The plant is an excellent companion for timothy; it is less susceptible to clover rot and stem eelworm, but can cause bloat.

Yellow suckling clover *(Trifolium dubium)*

An indigenous annual plant, usually less than six inches in height. Grows well in dry pastures and is a nutritious forage plant. A relatively vigorous variety known as "English giant red suckling clover" has been grown on a small scale in eastern England for many years.

Suitability of legumes for different environments

The suitability of the legumes described above is summarised in Table 3.1 for different soil types, rainfall and management requirements.

References

Russell, E.J. 1954 *Soil Conditions and Plant Growth*, Eighth Edition, 635pp.
Lampkin, N. 1991 *Organic Farming*, Farming Press, 701pp.
Spedding, C.R.W. & Dickmahns, E.J. 1972 *Grasses & Legumes in British Agriculture*. CAB Bulletin 49, 511pp.

Table 3.1.   Legumes and their appropriate environments.

Soil Type	Rainfall	Requirement	Suggested legume	Problems
Lowland, calcareous soil (pH6-8)	Low, 26" or less	Long ley, conservation /grazing quality animal performance	1. Lucerne 2. Sainfoin	Wilt, bloat Expensive seed
Strong, poor calcareous soil (pH6-8)	Low	Grazing, long ley	1. Kidney Vetch 2. Yellow suckling clover	
Poor, light land (pH6-7)	Low	Soil improvement Green manure	1. Blue Lupin 2. American sweet clover	Lupinosis Unpalatable
Lowland, calcareous soil (pH6-7.5)	Average	Short rotation (2 yrs) Conservation, grazing	Red clover	Eelworm, clover rot, bloat, oestrogenic
"	"	Long rotation (3-4 yrs) Conservation, grazing	1. Red clover 2. White clover - medium large leaf	Eelworm, clover rot, bloat
Average soil (pH5.5-6.5) lowland/upland	Average/wet	Permanent pasture, grazing	White clover, small leaf	Bloat
Poor land (pH5.5-6.5)	Wet, 40" & over	Grazing, soil improvement	1. Lotus 2. Alsike clover	Bloat
Any soil type	Average	Grazing	Trefoil	

RED CLOVER,
EARLY-FLOWERING
(*Trifolium pratense* L.).

WHITE CLOVER
(*Trifolium repens* L.).

YELLOW TREFOIL ; NONSUCH ; ' HOP ' CLOVER ; BLACK MEDICK

(*Medicago lupulina* L.).

Chapter 4

Herbs

Should herbs, which are expensive, be included in seeds mixtures or not? Foster (1988) in a recent review ends on a cautionary note, emphasising that it is still not known whether herbs have a beneficial effect on the grazing animal, apart from introducing dietary variation, or even whether the deep rooted herbs help to break up soil pans. She also makes the case for the development of more competitive strains of the most useful herbs. One of their shortcomings is that they don't last very well, mainly, it seems, because they are so popular with livestock that they are grazed out of the sward.

What exactly is a herb? In the broadest sense a herb is any broad-leaved plant, most of which tend to be called weeds when appearing in grassland, for instance thistles, docks and nettles. Newman Turner makes the point that they are only called weeds because man has failed to find a use for them. Herbs therefore are defined here as useful broad-leaved plants. The ones that have been found of most value and which will be discussed in this chapter are: chicory (*Cichorium intybus*), salad burnet (*Poterium sanguisaba*), ribgrass (*Plantago lanceolata*), sheep's parsley (*Petroselinum crispum*) and yarrow (*Achillea millefolium*).

Newman Turner and Friend Sykes were both enthusiastic advocates of the herbal ley. Newman Turner described it thus: "The herbal ley is my manure merchant, my food manufacturer and my vet, all in one".

Chicory

First sown in England in 1788 by Arthur Young who had noticed it used in France by progressive farmers. His crop of chicory grew nearly 75 tonnes fresh weight per hectare per annum, and was always eaten down to the ground by sheep, cows and bullocks. Pigs and horses also enjoyed it and the crop had the advantage of thriving on poor land and in drought conditions. As for its durability, he planted twelve acres in 1790 with a mixture of plants, amongst which were chicory and burnet and ten years later "much chicory was visible".

Robert Elliot used it in his seeds mixtures at Clifton Park on thin soil in the Scottish lowlands, and Friend Sykes included it either for limestone land or heavy land.

Newman Turner found it to be third favourite for palatability with his dairy cows of 35 trial plots (sheep's parsley and plantain were first and second), but chicory produced the greatest bulk. It produced many more cuts or grazings than any other ingredient of the ley mixture - when sown alone. He also recommends it as providing a rich source of all the minerals, trace-elements, vitamins and plant hormones.

Burnet

Elliot describes burnet thus: "Its principal use is for a sheep walk, and especially on poor hungry soils". Starts growth at the beginning of March and is useful for grazing throughout the year. One acre was believed to be "equal in consumption to any acre of the turnips". Unfortunately this is not a very exact measure of productivity. Apparently, when grown on some lands it acquires "a peculiar quality which makes it so unpalatable to cattle that they will not eat it". Newman Turner found, however, that burnet was eaten freely by his cows. In fact he rated it fourth out of thirty-five for palatability, and ahead of any of the grass species he sowed.

Elliot farmed light land at Clifton Park, the soil having a hard pan. He found that the roots of burnet penetrated this pan, descending to 72 cm. Newman Turner reckoned that because of its deep roots it was able to bring calcium up to an acid top soil. He recommended sowing it alone without a cover crop, but Sutton states that when sown alone it becomes coarse and unpalatable, but will be eaten when associated with more tempting herbage.

Ribgrass (long-leaved plantain)

Regarded by Sutton as a weed. He complains that the seed is one of the most frequent impurities of red clover. Newman Turner, on the other hand, regarded it highly, coming second in his cattle's order of preference. He regarded it as one of the most mineral-rich of all herbs, a view supported by Stapledon who recommended it where levels of calcium and phosphorus in the diet both need to be improved.

Ribgrass provides grazing in the autumn and winter. It forms a flat rosette when grazed hard, or when soil conditions are adverse but this enables it to persist. It grows taller on fertile soils.

Sheep's parsley

The favourite herb, despite its name, for Newman Turner's cattle, "grazed down hard before any of the others". Regarded as highly mineral-rich, and containing apiol, which has a potent beneficial effect on kidney and bladder complaints. It is also useful as a source of iron and of all the known vitamins. Newman Turner prized it as his own favourite raw snack. Sutton agrees about its palatability to sheep and thought it might be a preventive of red-water disease. Unfortunately, reliable data on its productivity and persistence are lacking.

Yarrow

A very useful constituent of permanent pastures, particularly during periods of drought. It needs to be kept short by sheep: otherwise it tends to smother out both grasses and clovers. It appears to be independent of the presence of potassium in the soil, and flourishes where clover will fail altogether. Will be reduced by the application of ammonium compounds. Regarded as useful for sheep on poor soils. Elliot maintained that it cured diarrhoea in his sheep. Unfortunately he does not state whether this was scouring caused by parasites, or what.

Dandelions

These have a high digestibility and have been shown to increase the milk yield of dairy cows by 10%.

Herbal mixtures

Newman Turner used herbs for early-grazing mixtures, midsummer and autumn and winter grazing. He also had herbal ley mixtures for thin, dry soils, all purpose leys, hedgerow mixtures, heavy land and a pig and poultry leys. The majority of these mixtures contain over 45 kg of seed/hectare. It is worth quoting his mixture for thin, dry sandy soils and comparing it with that of Friend Sykes for calcareous soils.

Newman Turner Thin, dry soils	kg per hectare	Friend Sykes Calcareous soils	kg per hectare
Cockfoot S143	5.5	Cocksfoot	5.5
Crested Dogstail	4.4	Perennial Ryegrass	4.4
Tall Fescue	4.4	Italian Ryegrass	1.1
Lucerne	4.4	Timothy	3.3
Kidney Vetch	4.4	Crested Dogstail	1.1
Chicory	4.4	Rough Stalked Meadow Grass	1.1
Burnet	4.4	Wild White Clover	1.1
Ribgrass	4.4	Broad-leaved Clover	2.2
Late Flowering Red Clover	2.2	Alsike	1.1
Alsike	2.2	Lucerne	3.3
Trefoil	2.2	American Sweetclover	2.2
S100 White	1.1	Burnet	2.2
Yarrow	0.5	Chicory	2.2
American Sweetclover	2.2		30.8 kg
Broad-leaved Plantain	1.1		
	48.0 kg		

Newman Turner's mixture contains only 30% grass, 39% legume and over 30% of herbs! Friend Sykes uses 53% grass, 32% legume and 15% herbs. Elliot's Clifton Park mixture includes 27% herbs.

If herbs are to play a significant role in organic farming, either because of their nutritional value on poor soils, or because of their medicinal properties, then experiments need to be conducted to prove their real worth. If this can be firmly established, then grazing trials must be carried out to ensure that the money spent on the herbal part of the seeds mixture is justified by knowing how to keep the herbs present in worthwhile proportions, for the duration of the leys.

References

Lyndall Foster 1988 *Herbs in pastures: development and research in Britain*, 1850-1984. Biological Agriculture and Horticulture, 5, 97-133.
Newman Turner 1955 *Fertility Pastures*. Faber and Faber, London, 204pp.
Elliot, R. 1908 *The Clifton Park System of Farming*, Fourth Edition, Simpkin Marshall Ltd, London.
Friend Sykes 1951 *Food, Farming and the Future*. Faber and Faber, London, 294pp.

Chapter 5

Temporary Grassland

Of the 18.5 million hectares of agricultural land in the United Kingdom, just over 9% is classified as temporary grassland. This area, 1.7 million hectares, is 10% less than in 1980. There has been a corresponding reduction in the purchase of grass and clover seed from 21,200 t to 17,800 t per year over the same period.

The regions that have most temporary pasture are the Grampian region of Scotland, Northumberland, South Yorkshire and Hampshire.

Grassland and organic farming pioneers such as Sir George Stapledon, Friend Sykes and Newman Turner all regarded the long ley as the key to maintaining the structure of the soil and improving the yield of arable crops. Stapledon was strongly of the opinion that certain land under permanent pasture would be much more productive if converted to temporary pasture, and that livestock would be less prone to disease if grazed on temporary leys, mainly because the land would be rested from animals during the arable phase.

A number of permanent pasture fields are of below-average fertility. Instead of improving these fields, the poorer performance is accepted by the farmer as a way of reducing costs, because ploughing-up and reseeding are expensive. The question is whether reseeding can be justified economically?

Humus

Central to the long term structure of the soil and to the use of the ley in an arable rotation is the role of humus. What is humus, what does it do and how can it be increased?

Humus has been defined as an indefinite brown acid substance, derived principally from lignin, which is a plant component very resistant to bacterial attack, and also derived from protein. The excretions and cells resulting from microbial metabolism also contribute to humus in the soil. Humus can be divided up into various fractions chemically. These are: humus, for the fraction insoluble in alkali, humic acid for that soluble in alkali but insoluble in acid; and fulvic acid for that soluble in both alkali and acid.

Humus has three main functions: it can absorb considerable quantities of water, and thus prevent water and nutrients from being leached through the soil profile, it can take part in base exchange reactions, and it plays an important role in the formation of soil crumbs, thus improving soil structure.

The effect of continuous arable cropping on levels of nitrogen and carbon and on the macro-organic content (humus) are shown in Table 5.1. These figures are based on long term experiments, each of 30 years, one at Rothamsted Experimental Station from 1894 to 1924 and the other at the Grassland Research Institute, Hurley between 1955 and 1984.

Table 5.1. Long term effect of continuous arable cropping on the content of carbon and nitrogen in the soil.

	Carbon %	Nitrogen %
Rothamsted (no manure or fertiliser)		
Initial value	2.04	0.218
After 30 years continuous wheat	1.28	0.131
Hurley (45 kg N, 20 kg P, 56 kg K annually)		
Initial value	1.2	0.13
After 30 years continuous spring barley	0.83	0.10

By contrast the effect of laying pasture down to permanent pasture is shown in Table 5.2.

Table 5.2. Effect of permanent pasture on the carbon and nitrogen content of the soil.

	Carbon (%)	Nitrogen (%)
Rothamstead (no manure or fertiliser)		
Initial value	1.14	0.108
After 23 years	1.23	0.145
Hurley (45 kg N, 20 kg P and 56 kg K/ha per ann.)		
Initial value	1.2	0.13
After 30 years	2.0	0.20

Under annual tillage at Hurley the decline in weight at plough depth was approximately 290 kg of carbon per ha per year and 25 kg of nitrogen per ha per year. Under pasture, the weight of carbon increased by 1000 kg per ha per year and nitrogen by 75 kg per ha per year.

Under arable cultivation the macro-organic matter to 15 cm depth, defined as "those organic materials retained on a 0.25 mm mesh sieve" fluctuated between 3 and 4 t/ha when sampled in November after ploughing, and amounted to 7-9% of the total soil carbon. Under pasture the macro-organic matter increased annually to reach 16 t/ha.

Rotations involving legumes

The arable farmer, who is dependent on cereals to maintain his income, cannot afford to put down his arable fields to permanent pasture. Instead he uses grass/legume leys, or a break crop such as rape or potatoes.

It was shown at Rothamsted that a three-course rotation of maize-wheat-clover reduced the loss of carbon and nitrogen after 30 years, compared to continuous wheat, and that sowing clover every three years was more effective in arresting this decline than a five course rotation of maize-oats-wheat-clover-timothy.

Legumes in the grass ley normally enrich both the soil and the companion grass with nitrogen. The way this is achieved is probably through nitrogen products being liberated into the soil when the nitrogen-rich modules are shed from the roots. Nodule shedding occurs quite frequently in perennial legumes, because the nodules are shortlived. Nodule shedding is increased by cutting or grazing.

Forage legumes such as clovers and lucerne normally add much more nitrogen to the soil than the grain legumes, such as beans, peas or soybeans. One of the reasons for this is the difference in root structure. Annual legumes such as peas have a restricted root system which nodulates over a short space of time, whereas the root system of clovers and lucerne grows throughout the year and will therefore form new nodules for a much longer period.

Estimates indicate that clovers and lucerne may add between 150 and 200 kg of N per ha per annum to the soil. Some of this will come from the decay of nodules, some may be excreted directly into the soil, and some will be in the living and dead root fibres. The amount of root fibres added to the soil annually has been estimated at 2.5 to 5 t per ha for lucerne. This compares with 0.6 t per ha from a cereal crop.

Different grasses have been shown to have different effects on soil structure and this is thought to be related to the weight and tensile strength of their roots. Strong roots are much more effective as soil-binding agents than very fine weak roots, even though there may be more of them.

Besides lignin-derived material from humus and roots, it has been shown that wormcasts are important for forming water-stable crumbs. A comparison between the number of water-stable crumbs in the top 3 inches of soil in an arable soil and a three year ley is shown in Table 5.3.

Table 5.3. The proportion of water-stable crumbs in the top 3 inches of soil and in wormcasts.

	Top 3 inches of soil	In wormcasts
Arable	7	19
3 year ley	46	58

The wormcasts on the arable soil have a better structure than the soil itself, yet the improvement brought about is much less than that brought about by a 3 year ley, and the ley improves the structure of the whole soil.

The ley break in the arable rotation has three main functions : to improve soil structure, to enhance the nutrient status of the soil, particularly the N level, and to reduce the incidence of plant disease. The effect of the ley on soil structure depends on the constituents of the ley and on the length of time the farmer leaves the ley down (Table 5.4).

Table 5.4.   The effect of the ley on water stable crumbs

Previous cropping	% of water stable crumbs > 2 mm
Old arable	4
3 years lucerne	20
3 years clover	35
6 years lucerne	30
old meadow	79
(from Russell, 1954)	

A three-year lucerne break has increased structure compared with arable by a factor of 5. Extending the lucerne break from 3 to 6 years has increased the proportion of water soluble crumbs by 50%. In this instance clover had a more beneficial effect than lucerne; but clearly the best soil structure was found under the old meadow. The speed of improvement in soil structure depends on soil type. It was shown at Hurley that after 8 years in pasture the level of macro-organic matter remained relatively stable. It may well be that one of the causes of the long ley improving soil structure is simply the absence of cultivation.

Although wheat has been grown continuously for more than a 100 years on the same land at Rothamsted, the yield is less than half that of wheat grown in rotation. In the same way, legumes should not be grown continuously because they are likely to suffer from disease.

When legumes are used in rotation they increase the nitrate content of the soil and this is correlated with the subsequent yield of cereal, in this case wheat (Table 5.5).

Table 5.5.   Effect of clover and grass on nitrate level in the soil, and on the subsequent wheat crop.

Treatment	Nitrate-N (ppm)	Subsequent wheat yield(t per ha)
Fallow	22.6	3.85
Clover	21.3	3.21
Clover/ryegrass	17.7	2.70
Ryegrass	13.6	2.21

The use of clover instead of ryegrass boosted the subsequent wheat yield by 50%.
The length of time that the legume in the ley benefits subsequent cropping is open to question. Some experiments show that the benefit may last for 3 to 5 years after the legume has been ploughed up, but the effect decreases markedly after the first year. The reason for the longer effect is the slow rate of breakdown of the legume root system, with the consequent slow release of N, P and K and calcium into the soil.

As mentioned earlier Stapledon, the Director of the Welsh Plant Breeding Station in Aberystwyth, was convinced that the most certain way of improving permanent pasture was to plough and reseed with a mixture of mainly perennial ryegrass and white clover. And to a large extent this policy was followed during the Second World War. However, there is now clear evidence, albeit from cutting trials and not from grazing, that the advantage to a reseed occurs mainly in the first year after sowing. The most likely reason for this is the mineralisation and subsequent increased availability of nitrogen from the ploughing up. If the reduction in yield during the seeding year is taken into account, then after the first three years reseeding can actually reduce productivity, particularly with no added fertiliser nitrogen.

The only other advantage of reseeding is the opportunity to introduce white clover, but techniques such as strip seeding into permanent pasture, are now available without having to have recourse to the plough.

The results from a cutting trial across 16 sites in England, from a range of elevation from 7 to 400 m, are shown in Table 5.6.

Table 5.6.   Herbage dry matter production (t per ha) with an 8-week cutting interval and no added fertiliser.

Treatment	Year 1	Year 2	Year 3
Perennial ryegrass reseed	7.05	5.72	6.56
PRG + white clover reseed	7.18	8.31	8.17
Permanent pasture	6.32	8.85	7.25

(from Hopkins *et al* 1990)

There was a considerable range in productivity between sites because of differences in inherent fertility, for instance at some sites the yield with no nitrogen was higher than that for some sites receiving 300 kg of N per ha.

It was clearly shown from this experiment that high levels of herbage production are obtainable from permanent swards of mixed species composition, even when the proportion of perennial ryegrass was very low or nil. It was also evident that, providing soil pH was satisfactory and there were adequate levels of P and K, then permanent swards are productive. The decision to plough up permanent pasture and resow an expensive seeds mixture should not be taken without a lot of consideration.

54

References

Hopkins, A., Gilbey, J., Dibb, C., Bowling, P.J. and Murray, P.J. 1990 *Response of permanent and reseeded grassland to fertilizer nitrogen.* 1. Herbage production and herbage quality. Grass and Forage Science 45: 43-56.

Russell, E.J. 1954 *Soil Condition and Plant Growth.* 8th Edition. Longmans, London. 635 pp.

Tyson, K.C., Roberts, D.H., Clement, C.R. and Garwood, E.A. 1990 *Comparison of crop yield and soil conditions during 30 years under annual tillage or grazed pasture.* Journal of Agricultural Science, Cambridge 115, 29-40.

Chapter 6

Permanent Grassland

Permanent grassland covers 11 million ha in Britain or 60% of the agricultural land - a vast resource. For every 1 ha of temporary grassland there are 7 ha of permanent pasture. These 11 million ha can in turn be divided into 5.2 million ha of grassland over 5 years old and 5.8 million ha of rough grazing. There is some debate as to when a temporary ley becomes permanent grassland, but the most usually quoted dividing line is 5 years. It would be a very slow arable rotation that would contain a ley break of over 5 years.

The distinction between grassland over 5 years old and rough grazing is not so clear cut. The most obvious difference is likely to be productivity but this is rarely measured in absolute terms. The term 'Grassland over 5 years' presupposes that at one time the field has been ploughed up and resown, but without accurate records this is hard to establish simply by botanical examination. The assumption is that rough grazing will be within land use capability classes 5 to 7, ranging from a severe to extremely severe degree of limitation for agriculture use. Factors preventing improvement are high altitude, extreme exposure, severe climate, excessively steep slopes, poorly drained boggy land, very stony parent material or bare rock.

Thus even without the use of fast-acting fertilisers there is a huge span in productive potential between a 'fatting' pasture in Leicestershire and a sphagnum-dominated bog on a Scottish mountain.

This difference is well-expressed in Table 6.1 which was drawn up by Boulet in 1939.

There is a twenty-fold difference in productivity, between the tall heather pasture and the drained temporary ley but this does not necessarily mean that one should convert all molinia into agrostis-dominated pasture. For, as pointed out by Hunter (1954), hill pasture swards must not be valued according to their productivity alone but according to the available grazing they afford at different seasons of the year. For instance, *Eriophorum vaginatum* (Bog cotton) was found to be heavily grazed by sheep in March, a time when there was little else on the hill. The Nardus sward was found to be well-used in November and December, when its autumn growth was winter-green. On most of the upland grazing the livestock, particularly the sheep, are outside every day of the year, and the less conserved food or concentrate the farmer has to feed the better, provided he is satisfied that his animals are getting enough nourishment. Shrubs and trees will also play their part, whether it is their leaves or seeds that are providing food, or as shelter or shade. That is why a brief description of their value is included in this book.

Table 6.1. Comparative grazing intensity (CGI) on different hill pasture swards (Temporary Ley = 100).

Sward Type	C.G.I.
Drained temporary ley	100
Agrostis	48
Festuca	33
Undrained temporary ley	27
Festuca (grazed) - heather	28
Festuca - nardus	18
Agrostis - nardus - molinia	18
Festuca - fern	14
Nardus - molinia	17
Wet molinia	7
Tall heather	5

Rough Grazings

Rough grazings are composed of four main types of plants:
a)   Dwarf shrubs, with heather (*Calluna vulgaris*) and the blueberry (*Vaccinium myrtillus*) being the most abundant and important.
b)   Grasses and Sedges. This includes white bent (*Nardus stricta*), flying bent (*Molinia caerulea*), wavy hair grass (*Deschampsia flexuosa*), tufted hair grass (*Deschampsia caespitosa*), sheep's fescue (*Festuca ovina*), red fescue (*Festuca rubra*), bent grasses (*Agrostis ssp.*), sweet vernal grass (*Anthoxanthum odoratum*) and Yorkshire fog (*Holcus lanatus*). The most prolific sedges include the deer sedge (*Tricophorum caespitosum*), bog cotton (*Eriophorum spp.*), and some of the sedges (*Carex spp.*). There are also a limited number of rushes (e.g. *Juncus squarrosus, articulatus and effusus*).
c)   Mosses and lichens. In excessively waterlogged or extremely exposed habitats, these may contribute the only vegetation e.g. *Sphagnum spp.* and *Polytrichum spp.*
d)   Ferns, with bracken (*Pteridium aquilinum*) being the most widespread and well known.

The nutritional value of trees

Tree leaves and seeds have considerable nutritional worth to animals in the uplands, as well as providing shelter and shade.
   Listed below are the ME value, digestible crude protein level (dcp) and digestible organic matter in the dry matter (D value) of some trees and their seeds, compared with gorse and heather.

Table 6.2. Nutritional value of trees.

	ME (MJ/kg DM)	DCP (g/kg DM)	D Value
Gorse	6.8	44	45
Heather	6.0	28	37
Elm leaves (dried)	10.3	132	65
Leaves of trees in July (dried)	9.1	74	55
Poplar leaves in Oct (dried)	9.7	72	53
Beech mast	15.2	121	66
Fresh acorns	13.6	54	83
Horse chestnut (fresh)	12.1	50	74
(from HMSO, 1975)			

Any leaf or tree seed is better nutritionally than heather or gorse in terms of energy, protein and digestibility.

Lowland and upland permanent pasture

The 5 million ha of permanent grassland in Britain is of great importance to organic and conventional livestock producers, coming between the grass of the temporary leys and the rough grazings. The main points that will be considered are: first, how productive is it and what stocking rate will it support (Chapter 7) and second, if it is of low yield, and a great deal of Britain's grassland has been condemned as in need of much better management, what methods are available to the organic farmer to improve it, economically (Chapter 8)?

References

Hopkins, A., Gilbey, J., Dibb, C., Bowling, P.J. and Murray, P.J. 1990 *Response of permanent and reseeded grassland to fertilizer nitrogen.* 1. Herbage production and herbage quality. Grass and Forage Science 45: 43-56.
Hunter, R.F. 1954 *The grazing of hill pasture sward types.* Journal of the British Grassland Society 9, 195-208.
HMSO 1975 *Energy Allowances and Feeding Systems for Ruminants.* Technical Bulletin 33, HMSO, London, 79pp.

Chapter 7

Assessing the productivity of grassland

Various attempts have been made to estimate grass yield, without actually having to measure it. There is agreement that the dominant factors are:

1) Soil type and depth
2) Grass growing days (which takes account of altitude and latitude)
3) Summer rainfall (potential moisture deficit)
4) Slope, trafficability. Useful for a knowledge of potential poaching. The organic farmer is less likely to want to apply fertiliser on a regular basis with a tractor.

All the above factors are important, and should be calculated initially to give some idea of the potential yield.

Also of importance in determining yield are i) soil nutrient status and pH ii) sward composition (particularly legume content).

There is nothing the farmer can do to alter the soil type, altitude, latitude or slope of his land, or the rainfall it receives each summer. But he can change soil nutrient status and sward composition. Conventional farmers who apply fast-acting fertilisers can swamp differences in sward composition by increasing the rate of nitrogen application particularly, but at a cost. This is the reason the predictive tables include response to increasing levels of nitrogen but ignore sward composition.

The other point that is of relevance is the question of accuracy of prediction of pasture yield. The factor that will always confound yield prediction is summer rainfall, and it is unlikely that long-term weather forecasting will become more accurate in the near future. The reasons for wanting to predict yield need considering.

First, particularly when taking possession of a new farm, is the importance of calculating stocking rate. How many animals, sheep and cattle, can the grassland maintain throughout the year? This includes conservation for the winter period. Winter feed is crucially important to the organic farmer because he cannot easily or cheaply bring in organic hay, let alone organic silage.

Second, it is very important that grassland is considered as a crop with a numerical yield, just like wheat or potatoes. It shouldn't be a dumping ground for an uncounted flock or herd. The use of each field of grass should be considered in the overall farm strategy. Which fields are likely to sustain lactation for how many animals, and for how long? Which fields are particularly suited to fattening bullocks or weaned lambs? What growth rate can be achieved? Predictions should be made, just as when calculating financial profit and loss, and then the actual results measured against the prediction, because only in this way can knowledge of grassland management increase and become more accurate. What did I expect from this field and what was the actual yield? It should all be recorded.

This leads to the third important consideration in prediction. When a field is under-performing then improvement can be carried out, providing the cause can be diagnosed. Yield assessment is necessary and of interest, to check whether improvement has actually occurred.

In the first instance, an accuracy of 10% would seem sufficiently large to be of importance and measurable.

Potential Yield

One of the earliest attempts to assess land potential was by Evans in 1951. He classified land by 'sustained oat yield', going from a maximum of 5.6 t/ha down to a minimum of 1 t per ha. This factor was then modified by annual rainfall, so that the best land with the highest rainfall (45-60 in per annum) required only 0.3 ha per food unit, and the worst at 15-25 in rainfall required 2.2 ha per food unit, a yield differential of 7.

Harrod (1979) nearly thirty years later compiled a table of grassland suitability, based on soil type, rainfall and trafficability, but he did not put actual yield values on any of his categories. However, his classification scheme forms the basis of a great many of the grassland suitability maps for England and Wales. The Meat and Livestock Commission (1978) and ICI (1981) both translated these results into dry matter yields. The yields, for grass receiving zero N or 150 kg N - equivalent to a good grass/white clover sward, adapted from MLC is shown in Table 7.1.

Table 7.1. Potential grassland yield from three soil types.

		Summer yield (t DM/ha)	
	Rainfall (mm)	0 N	150 N
Poor sites (chalklands), clay loams/silty loams	222	2.0	5.5
Average sites (Midlands), clay loams/silty loams	218	2.5	6.6
Good sites (Wales/S.West), silty loams/loams	311	3.2	7.2

Rather confusingly, clay/silty loams occur in the poor, average and good sites. In Milk from Grass (1981), the soil types have been redefined as:-
1. clay loams and heavy soils;
2. loams, medium textured soils and deeper soils over chalk;
3. shallow soils over chalk or rock, gravelly and coarse sandy soils.

Harrod (1979) has four basic soil classes for grassland suitability.

A. Soils are deep, mainly well drained, usually loamy or silty, brown soils, brown podzolic soils, or drained lowland peat soils or loamy ground-water gley soils. They occur on slopes less than 11º most often in moist areas, and are normally able to absorb excess rainfall swiftly.

B. Among soils in this group are brown soils with slight risk of drought, podzolic soils and lithomorphic soils in the moist zone, as well as many soils in the gleyic subgroups.

C. (i) Both gley and gleyic soils having high potential yields but poor trafficability and high poaching risk.

(ii) Many coarse loamy and sandy, stony or shallow, brown and podzolic soils in the dry zone.

(iii) Soils are often clayey surface-water gley soils, and pelosols with total available water far short of values needed to compensate for the large moisture deficits of the dry lowlands.

(iv) Stagnopodzols and loamy stagnohumic gley soils.

(v) Moderately steep and steep slopes (11-25º). Well drained brown soils, podzolic soils, or lithomorphic soils, are usual.

D. Very wet, economically undrainable soils, very wet peaty soils, extremely strong or raw soils, extremely rocky land. Soils included in this class are upland raw peat soils, clayey stagnohumic gley soils and humic gley soils; and brown, podzolic or lithomorphic soils on very steep slopes.

Harrod places much more emphasis on slope and drainage. But there is clearly disagreement about whether clay soils and heavy land should be in category 1 (Milk from Grass) or silty loams (MLC, Harrod). Potential yield and ease of utilisation must be differentiated. The heavier, wetter soils are high in potential but much harder to utilise, either by animals or machinery.

From the figures in Table 7.1 potential yield is likely to range from 2.0 to 7.2 t DM per ha, depending on site class and the amount of white clover in the sward. The effect of adding white clover in quantities greater than 25% to all grass swards receiving 0 N fertiliser is to double potential yield, at any site class.

In Milk from Grass (1981, 1st edition), 3 soil types and 3 categories of summer rainfall are given, see Table 7.2. The potential yield of grass with 0 Nitrogen is assessed as 1.7 t DM/ha for Site Class 5, 2.0 t DM/ha for Class 4, 2.3 t DM/ha for Class 3, 2.8 t DM/ha for Class 2 and 3.2 t DM/ha for Class 1. These yields agree neatly with those quoted by MLC, although the heavier clay soils have been placed above the silty loams as noticed earlier. Unsown grasses are described as yielding as much as perennial ryegrass in favourable conditions, but it is stated that the value of the lowland pastures is related to the content of ryegrass.

However, in the second edition of Milk from Grass (1992), the potential yield with 0 nitrogen is assessed at 5.1 t DM per ha for site class 5, and 5.6 t DM per ha for site classes 1 to 4. A huge change with very little explanation. These figures would now

62

Table 7.2.   Site classes

Soil Texture	Average April-September rainfall		
	More than 600 mm	300-400 mm	Less than 300 mm
Clay loams + heavy soils	1	2	3
Loams, medium textured soils and deeper soils over chalk	2	3	4
Shallow soils over chalk or rock, gravelly + coarse sandy soils	3	4	5

Add 1 for northern areas, i.e. Scotland - over 300 metres elevation
(from Milk from Grass, 1981)

suggest that apart from Site Class 5 there is no difference in yield between Site Classes 1 to 4.

Fields can be assigned to site class using two maps, one `Soil Suitability for Grassland' (Avery *et al*, 1974) and two `Grass Growing Days', both shown in Lazenby and Doyle (1981).

Having found a site class and a potential yield, then there is the question of whether the grass species and soil nutrient status allows this potential to be achieved. Most of the available evidence suggests that on both lowland and upland permanent pasture the proportion of perennial ryegrass or other sown species does not affect yield, provided that the sward is dense. This is particularly true in the organic situation, where no fast-acting fertiliser (N, P or K) is added.

The presence of more than 25% white clover by weight will raise potential yield considerably. A very open, sparse sward with moss will reduce yield, by as much as half, depending on amount of grass present.

In hillier and mountainous pastures, sward type reflects nutrient status. pH level and grass yield will be closely correlated with type of grass. Typical yields from these different hill pastures are shown in Table 7.3.

The other drawback to production in the hills is efficiency of utilisation, or rather inefficiency. Assuming lowland pasture, with N, to yield 10 t DM per ha and to carry 14 ewes plus lambs, then calculated food intake is approximately 7.5 t DM per ha, giving an efficiency of 75%. On hill pastures yielding 2 t DM per ha, the herbage ingested has been calculated as only 0.4 t DM per ha, giving an efficiency of 20%. This lowered efficiency is partly caused by less controlled management on the hills, which will lead to more wastage. As uneaten herbage matures and senesces, its

Table 7.3   Typical yield from hill pastures.

Sward Type	Base status	Typical yield (t DM/ha)
Nardus/Calluna	pH 3 to 6 (free drainage)	1.3 to 1.75
Molinia/Deschampsia	pH 3 to 4.5 (impeded drainage)	1.3 to 1.75
Agrostis/Fescue	pH 3 to 7 (flushed drainage)	2.2 to 2.75

digestibility quickly drops to levels below 60%, which makes it unpalatable even to hungry hill stock.

Measured yield

Using the potential yields calculated from Figs. 7.1 and 7.2 and the theoretical yields for the 5 site classes listed in Table 7.2, it is possible, using the data of Hopkins *et al* (1990), to check potential yield against measured yield. Yield was measured by exclosure cages and serial cutting, not by animal performance.

The results of the calculation of potential and measured grass yield of permanent pasture at 'O' level N are shown in Table 7.4. The most striking feature is that measured yield is double potential yield. Factors that might be responsible for this are first that Young and Thomas in Milk from Grass make the point that their figures are based on monthly harvestings but at the lowest summer rainfall expected in 7 years our of 10, and therefore represent the minimum yields to be expected in those 7 years. Second, the higher values for the measured yield could be caused by substantial amounts of white clover in the swards. However, Hopkins *et al* emphasise that many permanent swards, including some where perennial ryegrass and white clover are absent or are minor components, are capable of relatively high levels of production even with no N. So presumably lack of clover is not the cause.

Efficiency of utilisation

If the measured values of yield are more accurate than the potential values then the implications for organic farmers are very important: namely, that stocking rates and therefore output can be increased. However, as mentioned above, utilisation efficiency of grassland on the lowlands by the animal is likely to be about 75%, whereas utilisation on the hills is closer to 20%.

The most important step to be taken as a result of Table 7.4, for the organic farmer, is to re-check the yields for soil class A - D with a range of growing days, to concentrate on the 0 nitrogen situation, and to look very closely at the impact of the proportion of white clover on productivity.

In the joint study on the factors affecting the productivity of permanent grassland by ADAS and GRI (Forbes *et al*, 1980), output was measured in cow equivalents. One of the main findings was that there was a strong correlation between stocking rate and output. It should not however be assumed that the farms with the highest output had the highest potential grass yield. This follows on from the important premise that almost without exception the highest level of utilisation efficiency stems from the highest stocking rate. Output is therefore likely to reflect stocking rate rather than the potential yield of grass production.

Table 7.4   A comparison between potential and estimated grass yield.

Site	Site Class (Table 7.3)	'P' Potential Yield t DM/ha (Table 7.2)	'M' Measured Yield t DM/ha	M/P
1	3	2.3	3.9	1.7
2	5	1.7	3.5	2.0
3	5	1.7	4.6	2.7
4	4	2.0	4.4	2.2
5	2	2.8	4.2	1.5
6	5	1.7	4.0	2.3
7	5	1.7	3.3	1.9
8	5	1.7	4.5	2.6
9	4	2.0	4.5	2.2
10	3	2.3	6.2	2.7
11	3	2.3	6.1	2.6
12	5	1.7	4.3	2.5
13	2	2.8	3.4	1.2
14	3	2.3	5.0	2.2
15	4	2.0	2.4	1.2
16	3	2.3	4.5	1.9

Hopkins *et al*, 1990

The other point of significance to the grassland farmer is the length of the growing season and the rate of grass growth. This will be discussed more fully in a later chapter. Ideally, for ease of management, grass should grow at the same rate for every day of the year. The more compressed the grass growth curve is and the steeper the peak in the spring, the harder it is to utilise efficiently, particularly on steep or wet land where hay or silage making is difficult. This implies that the rougher permanent pastures are always going to be harder to utilise than temporary grassland.

References

Evans, T.W. 1951 *Land Potential.* Faber and Faber, London.

Forbes, T.J., Dibb, C., Green, J.O., Hopkins, A. and Peel, S. 1980 *Permanent Grassland. Factors Affecting the Productivity of Permanent Grassland.* The Grassland Research Institute, Hurley, 141 pp.

Harrod, T.R. 1979. Soil Survey Applications. Technical Monograph 13 (Ed. Jarvis, M. G. and Mackney, D).

Hopkins, A., Gilbey, J., Dibb, C., Bowling, P.J. and Murray, P.J. 1990 *Response of permanent and reseeded grassland to fertilizer nitrogen. 1. Herbage production and herbage quality.* Grass and Forage Science 45, 43-56.

Lazenby, A. & Doyle, C.J. 1981 *Grassland in the British economy - some problems, possibilities and speculations. Grassland in the British Economy,* CAS paper 10 (Ed. J.L. Jollans) 14-50.

Meat and Livestock Commission 1978. *Data summaries on upland and lowland sheep production* 27-33.

Thomas, C. and Young, J.W. 1981 *Milk from Grass* 104 pp.

Tivy, J. 1973 *The Organic Resources of Scotland.* Oliver and Boyd, Edinburgh. 227 pp.

Chapter 8

Sward Deterioration
and Improvement

To know that a sward has deteriorated it is essential to have in mind a clear idea either of what it should look like or what it should produce. What it produces should be measurable. When a pasture is sown down, or resown, then the farmer will assume that the new sward should contain the sown species, because otherwise why pay for the seed? Where permanent pasture is inherited, the farmer should have a clear idea (after a botanical examination) as to whether it can be improved, with what, and how.

The idea of perennial ryegrass being the best in all situations dies hard. But the clear outcome of a working party on sward deterioration in 1978 was that, in terms of animal output, performance was not, in any way, related to the proportion of perennial ryegrass in the sward, whether as a long ley or permanent pasture, particularly where nutrient status and inputs were low. Equally there was strong support for the crucial importance of white clover in the sward. If white clover was mismanaged, either by the addition of too much N or by inept grazing management, then the sward would certainly be less productive. Productive capability is the true test of deterioration, not the proportion of ryegrass.

Sward Composition

There are two very important concepts of sward composition. One is that pasture composition moves towards equilibrium with the environment. Continued change in composition implies either that the process of equilibration is slow or that the environment is not stable. The major factors affecting sward composition are nutrient supply, soil drainage and defoliation.

Change of sward composition from that produced initially by the mixture of species sown implies that the mixture is incompatible with the environment. This commonly occurs when swards rich in perennial ryegrass are sown in environments where the prevailing conditions cannot maintain a community with more than a small proportion of this species.

The second important concept is that botanical composition is a dependent variable and not a driving variable in the climate/soil/plant/animal system. Sward composition reflects what is happening to the system. The art of grassland management lies in being able to influence and control animal intake and production.

The consensus on sward composition is, first, that perennial ryegrass has an advantage in ease of establishment and initial production, which makes it valuable in short leys but not necessarily in permanent pasture. Second, that only if one of the main 'invading' grasses is *Poa annua* will there be a significant loss of yield.

In the study of the Park Grass plots at Rothamsted it was found that, on the unfertilised plots, *Agrostis tenuis* and *Festuca rubra* largely replaced *Lolium* and *Holcus* within about 15 years. And with increasing soil impoverishment there was an increase in the relative contribution made by broad-leaved weeds. The answer as to the effect of weeds on sward productivity would seem to be that only when dock content exceeded 20% would pasture yield be improved by eliminating them.

Reduction in the content of white clover is the first sign of decreasing productivity. Another sign of sward deterioration is the death of tillers, which are particularly vulnerable in the spring, the thinning out of plants (e.g. more bare ground), poor yields, reduced tillering, aerial tillering, disease damage, pest damage, sod-pulling, physical damage to the sward and to the soil.

Death of plants is often more rapid in short leys, than in long leys, which show more gradual changes.

A final point about factors influencing botanical composition: over a number of experiments and field observation it was found that soil drainage was often more important than soil texture in altering the sward composition of the sown leys. Rapid deterioration, at least to the *Poa* phase, was frequently associated with visual evidence of puddling or poaching.

Sward improvement

Sward improvement has two elements: one is the technical element as to how to do it, and the second is whether it is worthwhile financially.

There are three different contexts, the lowlands, the uplands and the hills. Each has a multiplicity of sward types, the main ones being a) grassy swards, b) *Nardus/fescue*, c) *Molinia/fescue*, d) *Eriophorum* (bog cotton) and e) *Calluna* (heather). Bracken is not normally classified as a sward type, but as an invasive weed.

In the previous section it was made clear as to why, in grassy swards, botanical composition was regarded as unimportant in deciding on sward improvement, with the notable exception of white clover. For the organic farmer a nitrogen-fixing legume is essential, and white clover because of its perenniality and its quality is the best legume for the majority of situations.

Grass-dominated swards (with the exception of *Nardus* and *Molinia*,) that are very open and with a high proportion of bare ground or moss, are worth considering for improvement. Very tussocky swards with a lot of senescent and dead material, or swards with disease and pest damage, or those where the ground is very poached and the sward damaged are also worth improving.

If a field is clearly in the above category, then three points must be considered before starting:

(1) The use to which the improved production will be put within the farming system. It is quite likely that fencing and stock control will also be required in order to benefit fully from the upgrading of the pasture.

(2) The economic consequences of utilising the additional pasture production, e.g. additional cost of new fencing and water supplies.

(3) The animal health implications of increasing the stocking rate or of buying in animals from other areas to suit the new grazing system.

Techniques for sward improvement

The techniques available for sward improvement can be grouped as follows, in order of preference.
1. Controlled grazing. The removal of pasture by grazing, when in a clean and relatively nutritious state, prevents the build up of dead plant material with its dilution of pasture quality and its reduction of photosynthesis. Furthermore, the increased grazing pressure and the enhanced return of animal excreta increase the quantities of the available N and P recycled.
2. Intensive grazing and cutting. For instance where useful *Agrostis/fescue* swards are being invaded by bracken, *Nardus* or *Molinia*, then cutting and intensive grazing, particularly with cattle, will help, but improvement will be slow.
3. Oversowing, without soil disturbance, or complete reseeding which is costly, and which will cause the built-up fertility and soil structure in long term permanent pasture to be released and possibly lost. But reseeding will produce the biggest change fastest. Problems that can occur when oversowing in wet conditions are the ingress of rushes and liver fluke, the onset of copper deficiency and poaching. In drier conditions there are the problems of puddling of the seedbed and the difficulty of removing surface trash. When cultivating for resowing, typical problems are fluffy seedbeds, the formation of soil pans, and rush and gorse ingress. When the sward climax is disturbed, the aggressive unwanted plants often colonise the quickest.
4. Drainage. This can mean anything from open sheep drains to tile drains at close spacing. There is evidence to show that the increase in herbage production and the longer grazing season resulting from expensive drainage are very rarely worth the cost involved.
    An alternative is to exclude the extremely water-logged areas from the enclosed paddocks.
5. Herbage destruction. Burning is the best method of removing old heather or *Molinia/Nardus* dominated swards, but great care is needed to keep the fires under control. It is also possible to use flail mowers to deal with heather.

Maintenance of improved swards

One of the chief problems with hill pasture improvement by reseeding has been the relatively rapid regression to the indigenous grasses that have just been replaced. This deterioration comes about because grazing management has been inadequate and because the required maintenance dressings of fertiliser have not been applied. Clearly this is a special problem for the organic farmer. The sowing of unsuitable grasses, selected primarily for high-fertility lowland conditions, may also be a contributing factor to sward regression.

Reference

Charles, A.H. & Haggar, R.J. (Eds) 1979 *Changes in Sward Composition and Productivity*. Occasional Symposium No. 10, British Grassland Society. 253 pp.

Chapter 9

Organic Fertilisers

To say that organic farmers are not permitted to apply any fertiliser to their land is untrue. Their main objective is to maintain, and if possible to increase, soil fertility, soil organic matter content and tilth. What they are discouraged from doing is to exploit the soil by continuous cropping, or to heap on fertilisers in a wasteful fashion so that streams become polluted with toxic levels of nitrate and their pastures become contaminated with heavy metals. Cultivations must not lead to an increased risk of soil erosion, nor should they deplete the finite energy resources. Organic farming is based on the proper treatment of the soil.

As far as organic grassland is concerned, the ploughing up of permanent pasture leads to the greatest risk of nutrient loss. Any fertilisers added to either permanent or temporary grassland must be used by the growing plant and not be leached through the soil profile.

The debate, referred to earlier, about weed grasses being less productive than perennial ryegrass is more a question of adequate soil nutrition. If the soil contains plenty of N, P + K and balanced trace elements and is of pH 5.6 to 6.2, then 'weed' grasses will produce as much dry matter as perennial ryegrass. The key to grassland productivity is not the grass species present, but the state of the soil.

The organic farmer cannot use the following fast acting fertilisers on his grassland: Nitrochalk, ammonium nitrate or urea, superphosphate, muriate of potash, kainit, slaked lime, quicklime or any compound fertilisers. But he can use composted farmyard manure, slurry, poultry manure from approved systems, basic slag, rock phosphate, rock potash, ground chalk and limestone and, under special circumstances, sulphate of potash.

Providing that there is plenty of white clover in the sward, nitrogen supply should not be a significant problem. The same is true of good permanent pasture that is grazed.

Applications of slurry and farmyard manure should not be made in late autumn or winter because their nutrients will be leached through the soil profile and increase the risk of polluting rivers and streams. They will contribute best during the spring and summer. If ground conditions are suitable they can be used as an early top dressing. If the field is going to be conserved as silage or hay, then farmyard manure should be applied at least 6 weeks before the crop is cut.

Lime and phosphates are often deficient on old pastures and without these the productive use of other fertilisers is reduced. Ground lime and basic slag should be applied on a regular basis, depending on pH and phosphate requirement. If the pasture is cut rather than grazed, then potash will also be required. The return of composted farmyard manure ensures the return of potassium, but the compost needs to be properly covered from the air and from the rain, so that losses of nitrogen and potassium are minimised, either by volatilisation or leaching.

There are three classes of poor pasture, which really need fertiliser;

1.   Poor clay land

Dung and other nitrogenous manures can be applied until white clover has been encouraged by the application of basic slag. If white clover does not increase in the year following the basic slag, then it should be introduced by slot-seeding or mob stocking; both should be carried out after as much of the grass has been cut as possible, for silage or hay, in late May or early June. The crucial factors in the successful establishment of white clover are first that it should not have to compete with grass during germination, second that the seed bed should be sufficiently moist and third that grazing in the first year to keep the grass in check should be with cattle rather than sheep. If sheep are used, then they should be mob stocked and the grazing be carried out as quickly as possible, e.g. within 3 days.

2.   Thin sandy soils

These are more difficult to improve than clays, partly because the soil is dry and partly because nutrients are easily leached through. The use of dung is valuable, to increase the organic matter in the soil.

3.   Thin chalky soils

The most essential manure on chalk soils is dung, but as with sandy soils only limited amounts should be applied because of the wastage. It is better to build the pastures up slowly by repeated small applications during the growing season. The improvement of poor grassland by a judicious combination of the right nutrients and good grazing management is a slow process.

Nitrogen

Nitrogen is essential for plant growth, as it is a constituent of all proteins and hence of all protoplasm. It is generally taken up by plants either as ammonium or nitrate ions, but the absorbed nitrate is rapidly reduced, probably to ammonium. The more nitrogen is supplied, the greater the amount of leaf area available for photosynthesis.

As leaf growth is increased by increased nitrogen supply, so synthesised carbohydrates are converted more rapidly to proteins and to protoplasm. The effect of increasing the proportion of protoplasm to cell wall material, has the effect of increasing the size of the cells and giving them a thinner wall, which makes the leaves more succulent. It also increases the proportion of water and decreases that of calcium to dry matter. Excessive amounts of nitrogen produce leaves with such large thin-walled cells that they are more readily attacked by insect and fungus pests and harmed by drought and frosts. A very low nitrogen supply on the other hand gives leaves with small cells and thick walls, and these leaves are harsh and fibrous.

The most noticeable effect of nitrogen is on leaf colour. The leaves of plants growing with a low level of nitrogen compared with other nutrients are pale yellowish to reddish green, which darken rapidly as the nitrogen supply increases, and become very dark green when it is excessive.

The response to nitrogen differs from the response to potash and phosphate in being relatively independent of climate if the rainfall lies between 22-40 inches, but they are reduced in years of drought or excessive rain.

Phosphorus

Phosphorus plays a fundamental role in the very large number of enzymic reactions that depend on phosphorylation. It is a constituent of the cell nucleus and is essential for cell division and for the development of meristem tissue. Phosphate deficiency is widespread in the world. In Britain it can be very marked on some of the clay soils of the midlands and on the acid millstone grits of northern England.

Crops tend to be more responsive to phosphate fertilisers in the higher rainfall areas of the west, though whether this is due to the crops having a higher phosphate demand in wet years, or whether it is a reflection of the tendency for the soils in the moister regions to be more acid, and therefore stronger fixers of phosphate in an unavailable form is not fully known.

Phosphate deficiency is extremely difficult to diagnose in the crop. Phosphate deficient crops have a stunted root system and a stunted leaf and stem. Phosphate seems to increase leaf area without affecting the power of the leaves to transport carbohydrates to the roots, and it thus differs from nitrogen manuring, which also increases leaf growth but reduces their power of sending carbohydrates to the roots.

Plants are relatively inefficient users of phosphates in the field, for rarely more than 20-30% of the amount supplied as fertiliser is taken up.

Potassium

Potassium is one of the essential elements in the nutrition of the plant, and one of the three that are commonly in sufficiently short supply in the soil to limit crop yield. Potassium is not part of the plant fabric, like nitrogen and carbon, but plays an essential part in its metabolism. Potassium plays an important role in the synthesis of amino acids and proteins from ammonium ions; it also assists in photosynthesis.

In the field, the potassium supply in the soil may be adequate for crops growing under conditions of a low nitrogen and phosphorus supply, but becomes inadequate if these are increased. Hence, signs of potassium starvation are often seen when only nitrogenous and phosphatic manures are given to a crop; the most characteristic sign is the premature death of the leaves.

Soils that are most likely to be deficient in potassium are light sandy or chalky soils and some peaty soils.

Trace Elements

The essential trace elements are: magnesium, iron, boron, manganese, copper, zinc, molybdenum, sulphur and calcium. The precise function of these trace elements is not yet known and they are sometimes toxic when present in more than very small quantities. Different plant species show different sensitivities to trace elements, and may display different symptoms. Sometimes it is not a case of an absolute deficiency of the element in the soil but rather a set of soil conditions which makes the element unavailable to the plant.

In organic farming, with the use of sound rotations, and with the encouragement of a wide range of plants in the sward, in addition to grasses, there is a good chance that there will not be a trace element deficiency in the sward.

Magnesium

Magnesium is needed by all green plants as it is a constituent of chlorophyll. It also plays an important role in the transport of phosphate in the plant. Magnesium deficiency often occurs on acid sandy soils that are also deficient in calcium. It can also be induced by unbalanced manuring, such as the excessive use of potassium fertilisers. It can be rectified by using a dolomitic instead of a purely calcareous limestone.

Iron

Iron deficiency typically shows up as a chlorosis, particularly on calcareous soils. Lime-induced chlorosis is the commonest of the iron deficiency chloroses. The trouble occurs on some of the zinc-rich soils derived from the dolomitic limestone in the Mendips. Farmyard manure and composts can sometimes be used to carry iron in a form available to the plant.

Boron

A shortage of boron typically affects the meristem, or actively dividing tissue, so that characteristic symptoms of boron deficiency are death of the growing points of shoot and root and the failure of the flower buds to develop. It can be induced by over-liming and it also shows up more strongly in dry than in wet seasons. The condition can be remedied by the addition of 10-12 kgs per ha of borax to the soil.

Manganese

Manganese has several functions in the plant. It is a constituent of some respiratory enzymes and of some enzymes responsible for protein synthesis. Manganese may also be concerned with the nitrogen metabolism of the plant.

Manganese deficiency typically occurs on calcareous or newly-limed peats, particularly if the water table is high. One method of reducing manganese deficiency is to make the soil more acid by the use of sulphur, for instance.

Copper

Copper plays a role in some of the respiratory enzymes and also in neutralising a harmful condition in the soil, such as inactivating harmful toxins.

Copper deficiency typically occurs on newly-reclaimed peats. In soils where the role of copper appears to be mainly as a nutrient, it is possible that there is an interaction between the need for zinc and for copper. Crops may respond to zinc if copper is also given.

Zinc

Zinc deficiency is more widespread in orchards than in grassland. It shows up more in climates with bright sunlight, and is usually restricted to heavy soils or to sandy soils containing peat. The power of a plant to extract zinc from the soil depends on the extensiveness of its root systems. Zinc deficiency can be cured by growing deep-rooted crops, such as lucerne, that are efficient extractors of zinc from soil and from subsoil.

Molybdenum

Leguminous plants are unable to fix nitrogen in the absence of molybdenum, and legumes can only be grown on some acid sandy soils if a dressing of ammonium or sodium molybdate is applied.

Sulphur

Sulphur is an essential constituent of many proteins. In New Zealand it has been shown that part of the benefit of applying superphosphate for legumes is the contamination of the slag with sulphur.

Calcium

Calcium appears to be essential for the growth of meristems and particularly for the proper growth and functioning of root tips. Calcium deficiency typically occurs on very acid soils. In general, farm crops are rarely limited by lack of calcium alone.

Calcium deficiency appears to have two effects on the plant: it causes a stunting of the root system and it gives a characteristic appearance to the leaf.

Farmyard Manure and Slurry

Table 9.1   **Nutrient availability from farmyard manure and slurries.**

	Nitrogen (N)	Phosphate (P2O5)	Potash (K2O)
Farm Yard Manure (kg/t)			
Cattle	1.5	2.0	4.0
Pig	1.5	4.0	2.5
Poultry			
deep litter	10.0	11.0	10.0
broiler litter	14.5	13.0	10.5
in-house air-dried	25.0	17.0	14.0
Undiluted slurry kg/m^3 (kg/1000 litres)			
Cow (10% DM)	1.5	1.0	4.5
Pig (10% DM)	4.0	2.0	2.7
Poultry (25% DM)	9.1	5.5	5.4

The available nutrients in manures and slurries from the various types of animal are shown in Table 9.1. The values are kg/t not percentage. It should be noted that the most valuable form of farmyard manure is from poultry. The management of animal manures is a crucial part of organic agriculture and they contribute a valuable resource which should not be dissipated. It is very easy to over-manure when using organic manures. In some countries, e.g. the Netherlands, limits to the quantity of manure which may be applied to the land are enforced by legislation. These limits, which are based on the quantity produced on a self-sufficient livestock holding, would be equivalent to 45,000 litres of fresh undiluted cattle or pig slurry per ha, or alternatively 40-50 t fresh farm yard manure (20-25 t composted) or 10-15 t poultry manure per ha.

The subject of composting farmyard manure, and the storage and application of slurry is more than adequately covered in 'Organic Farming' by Lampkin (1991).

Green Manures

The use of green manures for grassland is limited to their place in a crop rotation which includes temporary grassland. The effect of a crop as a green manure depends on its maturity when it is ploughed under. Nitrogen availability will only increase if readily decomposable material high in nitrogen, such as young green plants, is ploughed in. Humus content of the soil will only increase noticeably if fibrous plant material, fairly resistant to decomposition, is ploughed in. But such mature material will be lower in nitrogen than leafy young plants. Leguminous crops such as peas, clovers and some vetches are commonly used for green manuring because they comprise both leaves and fibrous stems.

Assessing fertiliser needs

Soil analysis can be carried out to determine soil type, humus, pH, calcium, phosphorus, potassium, magnesium, manganese, copper, iron and zinc. 25 sub-samples down to 6 inches should be taken per field and then mixed thoroughly. The analysis for other elements can be carried out by special request to most soil laboratories. Recommendations as to the best method of overcoming the deficiency are made within the cost of the service.

References

Hall, A.D. 1947 *Fertilisers and Manures*, Fourth Edition. John Murray, London, 333pp.
HMSO 1951 *Manures and Fertilisers*. Bulletin No. 36, HMSO, London, 96 pp.
Lampkin, N. 1991 *Organic Farming*. Farming Press, Ipswich, 701pp.
Russell, E.J. 1954 *Soil Conditions and Plant Growth*, Eighth Edition, Longmans, London, 635pp.
Soil Association 1989 *Standards for Organic Agriculture*. 80 pp.

Chapter 10

Weeds

It is useful to be able to define a weed. Newman Turner regarded weeds as a failure of man to use sufficient imagination or knowledge to find a role for them. For him there should be no such thing as a weed. Everything has a useful purpose, if it can only be discovered. However even he was hard pressed to find much use for couch grass apart from its yield. He listed its herbal properties but had to concede that it doesn't readily share a field with other crops. But this really is the point. A weed is something that is growing in the wrong place, for the farmer, and interfering with something that he is trying to achieve. The commonly cited instance is Italian ryegrass, which is sown as the major contributor of a short-term grass ley and then found to be a weed when it can't be eradicated easily from subsequent cereals.

The organic farmer cannot use the increasingly wide range of available herbicides, but on the other hand there is a growing feeling that some weeds are becoming resistant to herbicides and also that herbicide use creates problems of weed dominance by knocking out competitors. This points the way to longer-term control of weeds by correcting the deficiencies in the environmental conditions and management which have caused the weed problem in the first place.

Weeds are a problem because they flourish, and the reasons they do this are:

a)   because they are successful competitors with other plants for light, moisture and nutrients.

b)   because they have the ability to adapt rapidly to hostile conditions, using high genetic variability.

c)   many grow rapidly and form large quantities of seed or contain organs which gives them high regenerative capacity.

d)   the seeds are well adapted to being distributed and many remain viable for long periods of time, even when buried.

e)   they are often more resistant to diseases and therefore better able to compete with crop plants.

Weeds of permanent grassland

The main weeds of permanent grassland are docks, thistles, nettles, buttercups, bracken, rushes and ragwort. Several grass species such as Yorkshire fog and *Poa annua* are often classified as weeds but as has been shown earlier (Chapter 6), they can be both productive and palatable.

Docks *(Rumex spp.)*

Slurry and farmyard manure when spread on grassland often lead to heavy infestations of docks, especially on fields cut for silage. Docks have thick, fleshy tap roots which store food for the flowering shoots of the second and subsequent seasons. In undisturbed ground these tap roots can reach great size. If the tap roots are cut into fragments, they produce new shoots from pieces derived from the uppermost 7-10 cm. However, their main method of reproduction is by seed dispersal.

Over large areas, and with heavy infestations, it is impractible to dig them out by hand. The only alternative is first to graze them down as heavily as possible in the spring and early summer by sheep, and then to mow them before they get a chance to seed. This will slowly weaken them.

Thistles *(Cirsium arvense)*

The most troublesome thistle in permanent grassland is *Cirsium arvense,* the creeping thistle (purple flowers) which flowers between June and September, but there is also the prickly sow thistle *(Sonchus asper,* yellow flowers), which flowers from March to July and then again early autumn. Both these thistles spread by creeping roots, and in undisturbed ground the spread of creeping roots can be extremely rapid and extensive; up to 12 metres in a single year has been recorded for creeping thistle. New shoots from these roots appear in late spring.

In grassland, root spread is much slower because the grasses, particularly in tight-knit swards, suppress thistle root growth. The virtual dormancy of creeping thistle below grass swards is very prolonged, such that if the sward is ploughed, the clean looking pasture may yield an army of thistle shoots.

When flowering shoots are produced there is a considerable reduction of food resources in the roots. If the land is not to be ploughed up, then thistles should be mown when in flower (but not earlier, as this will encourage root development) and at regular intervals. If the land is to be cultivated, then they will eventually die, but only after intensive cultivation. A beetle *(Haltica carduorum)* of French origin was released in Britain for control of creeping thistle, but the climate proved unsuitable for it.

Nettles

Nettles spread vegetatively, with underground creeping stems, known as rhizomes. The effect is to suppress the grass underneath and to discourage animals from grazing near the nettle clumps. Nettles, like thistles, are high in protein, and can be used to make quality hay. They can be destroyed by repeated cutting at maturity, because, like thistles, earlier cutting strengthens the root system.

Buttercups

Creeping buttercup *(Ranunculus repens)* thrives in waterlogged soil, and drainage encourages it to disappear. Hard grazing in the spring also increases the proportion of buttercups by checking its natural competitor, grass. Liming to a pH of 6 or higher also helps to discourage their spread.

Bracken *(Pteridium aquilinum)*

Bracken is not only a weed but is also poisonous to stock. It has been shown to contain a carcinogen, shikimic acid, which might prove a hazard to humans if transmitted in cow's milk.

Bracken was originally a component of the herb layer of deciduous woodland, but with de-afforestation it has colonised thousands of hectares of upland pasture and rough grazing. The reason for its success, biologically, stems from its morphology.

Although it can reproduce sexually, with windborne spores, which enable it to colonise areas at a distance, it also has an extremely effective system of vegetative reproduction. This is based on a large rhizome system, which forms a huge underground storehouse of carbohydrate. When the emerging, or emergent frond is damaged, a dormant bud will develop and replace it. The rate of rhizome extension has been measured as 60-90 cm per annum.

The other attribute which has contributed to its success is its height and ability to cast shade. The shade thrown by the bracken fronds in summer is increased by the even deeper shade produced by the very heavy litter found beneath a bracken-stand in winter. This year-round depression of light is an effective weapon against its main colonising rivals, heather and grass.

When labour was plentiful, bracken was cut frequently for roofing and bedding material. There were also more cattle to trample the bracken fronds. But with the reduction in the human population on the hills, the decrease in cattle numbers, and the increase in sheep, bracken has flourished.

Bracken thrives best under a moderate to high rainfall and on freely-drained soils. It grows best in sheltered gullies where it is protected from late spring frosts and high winds.

Mechanical cutting can be used to control bracken, particularly in August when the fronds are at full maturity, when it is too late for frond replacement to occur, and before large quantities of carbohydrate have been transferred underground. But cutting needs to be repeated frequently and for several years, to exhaust the plant. Frequent treading by cattle will damage buds and the developing fronds which lie close to the surface. Pigs can also be used to root out the rhizomes, but they must be given other sources of food, to prevent poisoning.

If the land with bracken can be cultivated then the rhizomes should be cut up and then the process repeated, to cut the shoots growing from the buds. This needs to be continued until the budding process and the nutrient reserves are exhausted.

Rushes *(Juncus spp)*

Juncus spp produce very large numbers of seeds, estimated at 9 million per m^2 for a dense stand. Because these seeds are very small they will only germinate if near the surface (e.g. within the top 5 cm), otherwise light becomes a limiting factor. If disturbed by ploughing they may produce an enormous population of seedlings.

Rushes grow well in poorly drained swards so that one of the methods of control is improving the drainage. The other is to raise the pH by liming.

Ragwort *(Senecio jacobaea)*

Ragwort is poisonous to stock, but only when cut and wilted; to prevent ragwort being eaten, it should be cut and removed before a hay or silage crop is taken.

Weeds of temporary grassland

There are many possible weeds of temporary pasture, especially those which germinate easily when the soil is ploughed. But for the grassland farmer these weeds are not so much of a problem as the weeds of permanent pasture, partly because there is usually so much more permanent pasture on the farm and partly because if the field has been ploughed then cultivation is possible prior to re-seeding or sowing the next crop in the rotation. Cultivation is an easier method of getting rid of weeds than mowing or digging-up by hand.

Common weeds are: chickweed (*Stellaria media*), which can quickly grow into clumps and smother the emergent grass and clover seedlings; fat hen (*Chenopodium album*), which is large, and has tough, wiry stems; knotgrass (*Polygonum aviculare*); redshank (*Polygonum persicaria*); groundsel (*Senecio vulgaris*); field bindweed (*Convolvulus arvensis*); shepherd's purse (*Capsella bursa-pastoris*); barren brome (*Bromus sterilis*) and black grass (*Alopecurus myosuroides*), which have been favoured by the increase in winter cereals grown with reduced cultivations; charlock (*Sinapis arvensis*) and poppy (*Papaver spp*), which may remain viable for many years and will then germinate when its seed is brought to the surface.

This is by no means a full list, but the actual species which occur vary, depending on previous cropping, time and method of sowing. A guide to the identification of weed seedlings is on pages 83 to 96 (reproduced from "The Identification of Weed Seedlings of Farm and Garden", by R J Chancellor (1966), with the kind permission of Blackwells Scientific Publications, Ltd.). Most of the seedlings are 1.5 x actual size.

Dissemination of weed seeds

The most important route, especially in the past, has been via herbage seed which has not been properly cleaned. Hay used for feeding and straw for bedding may include weed seeds, commonly still on the stalks.

Compost, farmyard manure and silage may all contain weed seeds; the heat developed during composting rarely kills them, and even if high temperatures do occur, those in the outer layers are likely to survive.

Farm machinery can transport weed seeds, both within it and in mud on the wheels. Hooked or armed seeds cling onto sacks and clothing.

Birds and mammals may carry seeds internally or externally. A surprising number of seeds remain viable after passing through the digestive tract. It has been estimated that a single cow may distribute 900,000 viable seeds in its dung during the grazing season.

Some seeds get carried in the wind or on water. It has been estimated that in Oxfordshire 37 seeds of the perennial sow thistle fall on each hectare per annum.

The soil bank of weed seeds

As a consequence of dormancy, weed seeds are likely to be present on or in virtually all soils. In arable fields, operations such as discing and harrowing incorporate seeds into the soil throughout the working depth, whilst ploughing buries seeds which have recently been shed onto the soil surface.

In grassland which was formerly arable, large numbers of seeds of arable weeds may be found and may persist for decades. On uplands, heather (*Calluna vulgaris*) is often the most common seed found in the soil.

In arable soils there is usually an appreciable seed bank stemming from weeds in the previous crop. These reserves mean that continuing control measures are needed. The average number of viable seeds is $5000/m^2$ but the range is 1000 to 25,000 viable seeds/m^2. The most abundant weed seeds are normally annual meadow-grass, chickweed and fat-hen.

Experimental evidence suggests that the decline in seed numbers in the seed bank in cultivated soil is exponential, with losses of between 20-50 per cent per year. The rate of loss is greatest for seeds near the surface and when the soil is frequently cultivated. Although 95% of the seeds of chickweed may germinate in their first year after shedding, a proportion can survive for more than 60 years when buried in grass.

The three essential requirements for seed germination are oxygen, moisture and a suitable temperature. Oxygen is not usually limiting in soils unless conditions are very waterlogged. Moisture, however, can be limiting, with peaks of germination being associated with periods of heavy rainfall.

The response to temperature is more variable. Some species only germinate when the temperature is relatively high (e.g. *Chenopodium rubrum*), other such as the ivy-leaved speedwell (*Veronica hederifolia*) germinate best at low temperatures, and this determines the season at which they appear. Yet other species are able to germinate over a wide range of temperatures, e.g. annual meadow grass (*Poa annua*).

Light is also required for germination, particularly for small seeds such as *Juncus*. Seeds of other species which have been buried often need exposure to light, perhaps only for a very short time.

Periodicity of germination of weed seeds

Germination of the common weeds is shown in Table 10.1.

The distinctive patterns of weed emergence are maintained whether or not the soil is cultivated. Soil disturbance at a time within the emergence period causes an increase in the actual number of seedlings appearing, but cultivations at other times do not normally result in seedling emergence. Periodicity of germination is of great practical importance because it is a major factor determining the association of annual weeds with particular crops or cropping systems, according to the time of year at which the seedbed is prepared.

Table 10.1. Typical period of germinating weed seeds in the UK.

Dec, Jan, Feb	March, Apr, May	June, July, Aug	Sept, Oct, Nov
	Scarlet Pimpernel		Black grass
Shepherd's Purse	Shepherd's Purse	Shepherd's Purse	
	Fat-hen	Fat-hen	
Scented mayweed	Scented mayweed	Scented mayweed	Scented mayweed
Common Poppy	Greater plantain		Common poppy
Poa annua	Poa annua	Poa annua	Poa annua
	Knotgrass		Groundsel
	Black-bindweed		
	Redshank		
	Groundsel		
	Charlock		
	Prickly sow thistle		
Chickweed			Chickweed
	Small nettle	Small nettle	
Speedwell			Speedwell

Effect of cultivation on weed germination

Weeds may be able to establish more rapidly than the grass crop because their seeds have already absorbed moisture; their establishment may also be less dependent on soil tilth. However, appreciably greater numbers of weed seedlings usually appear on a fine, firm seedbed than on one which is left rough.

Because the losses from the soil bank of weed seeds after cultivation are relatively small, it is doubtful whether cultivations aimed at reducing the seedbank are worthwhile. A better method is to disturb the soil as little as possible, or avoid disturbance altogether, as when crops are grown with minimum tillage. Under these conditions seedlings arising from the seedbank will be minimal.

References

Roberts, E. 1988 *Weed Control Handbook:* Principles. Seventh Edition.

Lampkin, N. 1991 *Organic Farming.* Farming Press, Ipswich, 701pp.

Newman Turner 1955 *Fertility Pastures.* Faber and Faber, London, 204pp.

Tivy, J. 1973 *The Organic Resources of Scotland.* Oliver and Boyd, Edinburgh, 227pp.

Galium aparine
(Cleavers, Goosegrass, Herrif)

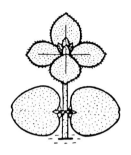

Sherardia arvensis
(Field Madder)

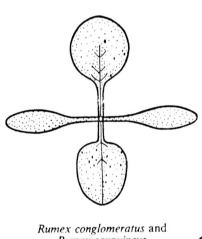

Rumex conglomeratus and
Rumex sanguineus
(Sharp Dock)
(Red-veined Dock)

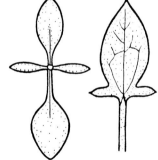

Rumex acetosella
(Sheep's Sorrel)

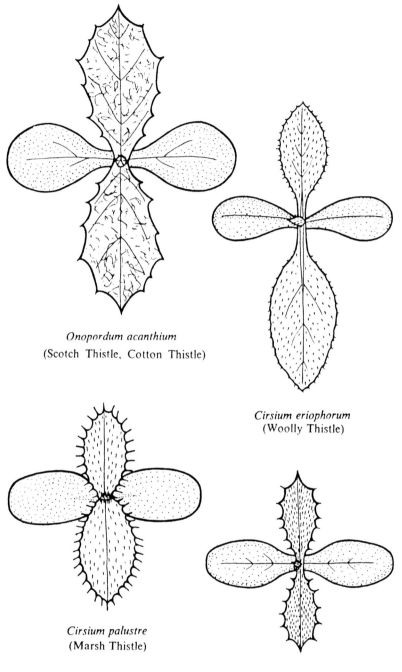

Onopordum acanthium
(Scotch Thistle, Cotton Thistle)

Cirsium eriophorum
(Woolly Thistle)

Cirsium palustre
(Marsh Thistle)

Cirsium arvense
(Creeping Thistle)

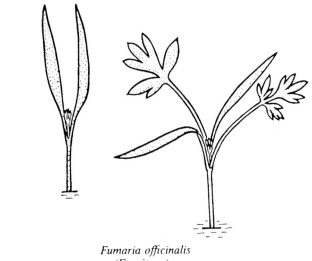

Fumaria officinalis
(Fumitory)

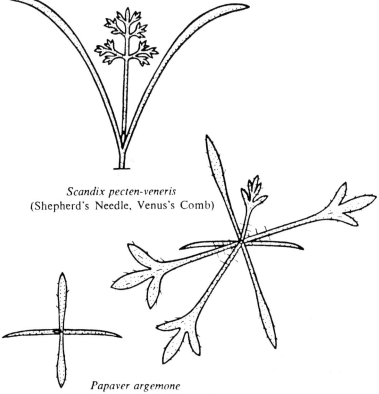

Scandix pecten-veneris
(Shepherd's Needle, Venus's Comb)

Papaver argemone
(Prickly Long-headed Poppy)

86

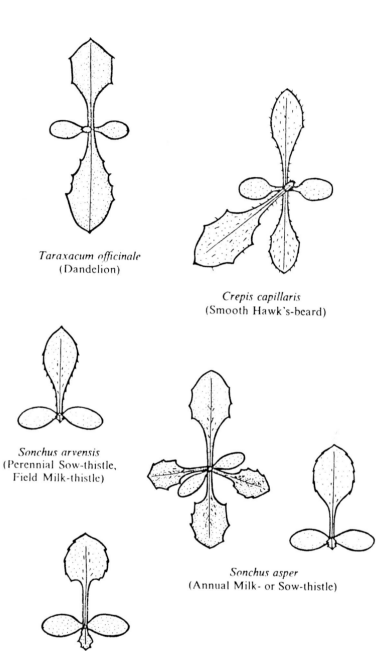

Taraxacum officinale
(Dandelion)

Crepis capillaris
(Smooth Hawk's-beard)

Sonchus arvensis
(Perennial Sow-thistle,
Field Milk-thistle)

Sonchus asper
(Annual Milk- or Sow-thistle)

Sonchus oleraceus
(Annual Milk- or Sow-thistle)

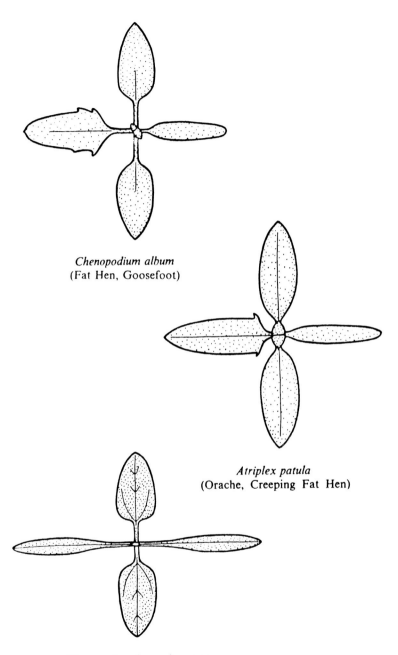

Chenopodium album
(Fat Hen, Goosefoot)

Atriplex patula
(Orache, Creeping Fat Hen)

Chenopodium bonus-henricus
(Good King Henry)

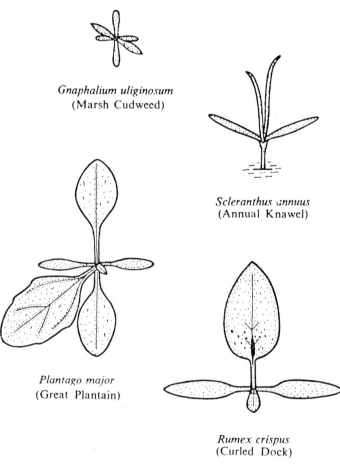

Gnaphalium uliginosum
(Marsh Cudweed)

Scleranthus annuus
(Annual Knawel)

Plantago major
(Great Plantain)

Rumex crispus
(Curled Dock)

Rumex obtusifolius
(Broad-leaved Dock)

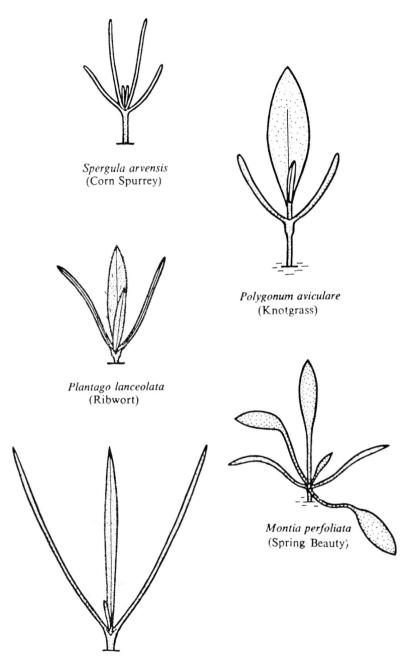

Spergula arvensis
(Corn Spurrey)

Polygonum aviculare
(Knotgrass)

Plantago lanceolata
(Ribwort)

Montia perfoliata
(Spring Beauty)

Tragopogon pratensis
(Goat's Beard, Jack-go-to-bed-at-noon)

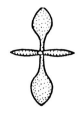

Papaver rhoeas, Papaver dubium
and *Papaver lecoqii*
(Corn Poppy)

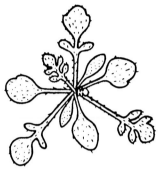

Papaver rhoeas

Papaver rhoeas

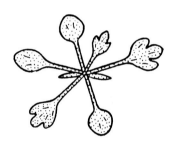

Papaver dubium
(Long-headed Poppy)

Papaver lecoqii
(Babington's Poppy)

Coronopus didymus
(Lesser Swine-cress)

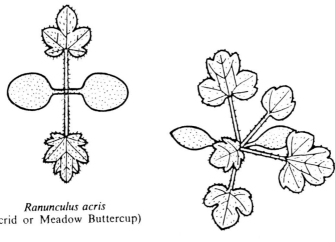

Ranunculus acris
(Acrid or Meadow Buttercup)

Ranunculus bulbosus
(Bulbous Buttercup)

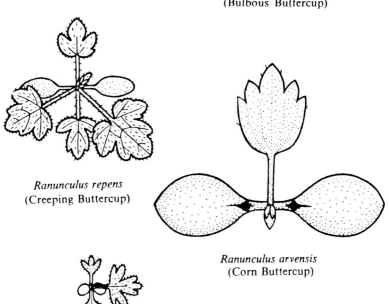

Ranunculus repens
(Creeping Buttercup)

Ranunculus arvensis
(Corn Buttercup)

Aphanes arvensis
(Parsley Piert)

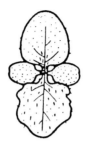

Mentha arvensis
(Corn Mint)

Senecio jacobaea
(Ragwort)

Senecio erucifolius
(Hoary Ragwort)

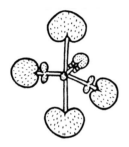

Cardamine hirsuta
(Hairy Bitter-cress)

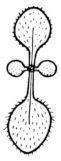

Conyza canadensis
(Canadian Fleabane)

Bellis perennis
(Daisy)

Stellaria media
(Chickweed)

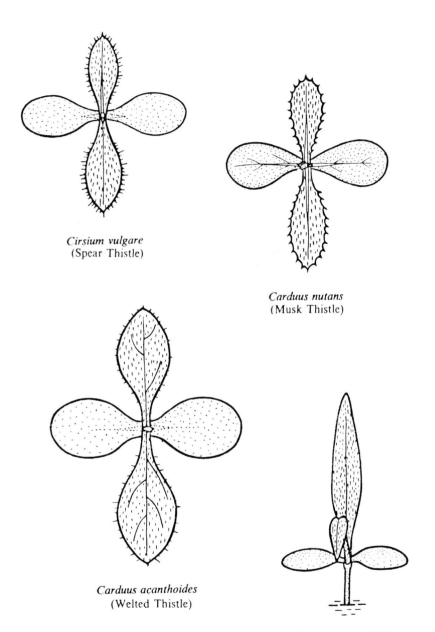

Cirsium vulgare
(Spear Thistle)

Carduus nutans
(Musk Thistle)

Carduus acanthoides
(Welted Thistle)

Polygonum lapathifolium
(Pale Persicaria, Willow Weed)

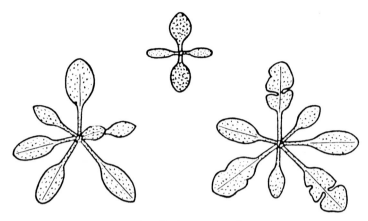

Capsella bursa-pastoris
(Shepherd's Purse)

Arabidopsis thaliana
(Thale Cress, Wall Cress)

Erysimum cheiranthoides
(Treacle Mustard)

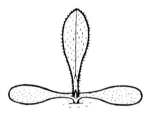

Picris echioides
(Bristly Ox-tongue)

Mercurialis annua
(Annual Mercury)

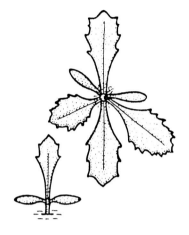

Senecio vulgaris
(Groundsel)

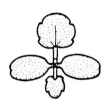

Viola arvensis and
Viola tricolor ssp. tricolor
(Field Pansy)
(Wild Pansy, Heart's-ease)

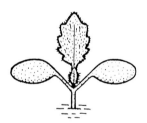

Senecio viscosus
(Stinking Groundsel)

Chamaenerion angustifolium
(Fireweed, Rosebay Willow-herb)

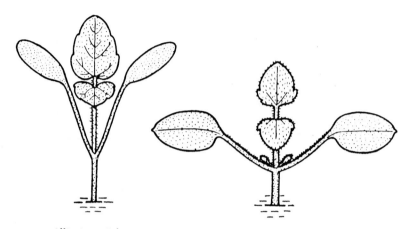

Alliaria petiolata
(Garlic Mustard, Jack-by-the-hedge)

Veronica hederifolia
(Ivy-leaved Speedwell)

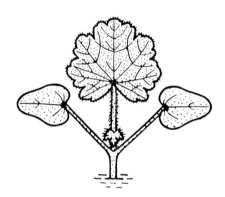

Malva sylvestris
(Common Mallow)

Chapter 11

Pests and diseases

Pests

It is not surprising that pests of grassland should be able to reduce dry matter production of the sward by 25%, when it has been estimated that the weight of leather-jackets alone in the soil may be as great as that of the grazing animals on top of the sward.

Permanent Grassland

Permanent pasture, undisturbed by cultivation, favours pest species with a long life cycle such as wireworms (*Agriotes*). Clements and Bentley (1985) found that grassland yield was reduced by a combination of plant-sucking bugs, soil-inhabiting Diptera and stem-boring Diptera. They also found that the proportion of sown grasses (ryegrasses) decreased with increasing sward age, whilst the proportion of unsown grasses increased. Coincidentally the grass yield to chemical pesticide treatment became less pronounced with increasing age of sward. Furthermore, when they tested the effect of pests on the yield of upland grassland, which also had less ryegrass and fewer frit fly, the response to pesticide treatment was less noticeable. Perennial ryegrass is known to be the preferred host of stem-boring Diptera, and both these experiments strongly suggest that secondary (or weed) grasses have greater resistance to pests.

Possible control measures for the organic farmer are heavy rolling and defoliating at critical times. A method of biological control, which is being explored in New Zealand, is the use of an endophytic fungus, which makes the grass more resistant to attack by a range of pests.

Another likely source of yield reduction is that caused by nematodes. The nematode life cycle starts with the hatch of juveniles in the soil. These then invade the roots of white clover, (*Heterodera trifolii* and *Ditylenchus dipsaci*) and develop asexually to females, feeding within roots. Eggs hatch on maturation so that several generations per year can be completed in moist soil with active clover growth. The females are preserved as cysts, which protect dormant eggs in cold or dry soils. Soil populations are often very low but multiplication within the host is rapid. Reductions in yield of clover of 8% have been established. The consequences of infection of clover with nematodes may be a reduced yield over short periods or longer term loss of clover in patches.

Another nematode (*Meloidogyne naasi*) infects grass, especially perennial ryegrass, but has much less effect on the fescues or on timothy and cocksfoot.

Temporary grassland

Pests that have been found to interfere with the establishment and productivity of temporary grassland are frit-fly (*Oscinella*), leather-jackets (*Tipula*), slugs (*Deroceras*), weevils (*Sitona*) and nematodes.

Prediction of the amount of damage is difficult because of the irregular pattern of pest infestation, with the sward being affected sometimes in patches and sometimes completely.

Pest damage is especially severe when grass swards are established using minimal cultivation techniques. Ploughing, followed by traditional seedbed cultivations, reduces the number of many insect species by desiccation, predation by birds and mechanical damage. This helps establishment, but the advantage tends to be short-lived, with numbers building back up.

The same has been found with the slot-seeding of white clover into permanent grassland. Vulnerable young clover seedlings emerge into an environment that is teeming with pests and nematodes.

The time of sowing is also important in reducing likely insect damage to temporary grassland. For instance frit-fly attack is more severe with autumn sown grass than with spring sown swards. The reasons are that populations of frit-fly larvae build up during the growing season and are highest in the autumn. This occurs on top of grass seedling growth that is less vigorous, and tillering that is less dense in autumn sown swards. The seedlings are therefore less able to grow away from pest attack.

Control measures

The choice of resistant species of grass and clover is the most effective method of reducing damage, a strategy not available with the management of permanent pasture.

Any husbandry that promotes vigorous seedling growth is valuable, but this doesn't necessarily mean increasing seed rate. Research is underway to establish the value of parasitic wasps to control frit-flies.

Diseases

Diseases of grassland such as Crown rust (*Puccinia coronata*) and Scald (*Rhynchosporium orthosporum*) affect palatability, and therefore utilisation, as well as depressing overall yield.

Fungi are always found in a wide range of species. *Fusarium* is the most common in grassland and *F. arthrosporioides* and *F. nivale* can kill plants, otherwise the damage has only a light or moderate effect on plant growth. Fungi can invade the root cortex as well as the vascular system and are characterised by intercellular growth and the formation of cell-wall swellings.

One of the principal characteristics of diseases in grasslands is that they often occur at very low levels, usually below 5% of the leaf area being damaged. However, a bad attack of crown rust will cause 15-20% loss of the dry matter in perennial ryegrass.

There are also several viruses that affect grasses and the legumes. Ryegrass mosaic virus infection may reduce yield by as much as 30%, but mainly in late conservation cuts. Barley yellow dwarf virus can also occur in grasses, cocksfoot mottle virus is lethal to the plant, as is clover rot. Red clover necrotic mosaic virus can cause losses up to 60%; it also reduces the content of leaf water-soluble carbohydrates by between

25-50%, making them less valuable nutritionally. Fortunately most herbage plants are outbreeders, ensuring a wide genotypic diversity which helps crop resistance.

Barley yellow dwarf virus causes pronounced stunting in all of its many grass hosts. By contrast, cocksfoot streak virus does not affect plant height but reduces total tillering capacity. With all these viruses, the rate at which compensation by uninfected plants in a sward proves sufficient to maintain sward vigour is dependent on the rate of infection.

Infection with ryegrass mosaic virus has also been suggested as a factor increasing the rate of winterkill. The amount of damage caused by virus infection is increased by the synergistic interaction between the virus and increased fungal invasion. If the plant has a virus, it has a greater chance of being infected by a fungus.

Control of grassland diseases on organic farms is limited to

1) Husbandry. The main objective is to avoid mature growth, either by frequent cutting or grazing. This reduces the risk of severe infection by leaf-spot pathogens. Autumn defoliation reduces mite numbers and helps to reduce the chance of winterkill. Old turf, lying on the soil surface when a ley is reseeded, also provides a source of virus and vectors.

2) Development and use of cultivars with improved resistance.

However, the organic farmer can take some comfort from the knowledge that viruses and other grass pathogens are likely to be of greatest importance in intensive management situations. The intensification of grass production, the growing of simpler mixtures or single species swards, the trend towards a narrower base in the genetic diversity of cultivars and the use of high nitrogen levels all lead to a situation which favours the development of disease epidemics.

References

Clements, R.O. and Bentley, B.R. 1985 Weeds, *Pests and Diseases of Grassland and Herbage* Legumes. in: Occasional Symposium, British Grassland Society. (Ed J.S. Brockman).

Chapter 12

Grazing Management

Like the best partnerships, grazing management is a compromise between the immediate requirements of the animal for food, and the longer term productivity of the sward. It is also a mixture of art and science, although agricultural research should be increasing its predictability. The problem in controlling sward composition is that it is a dynamic process. When animals are kept indoors and offered hay, then they eat what they want without affecting the meadow where the hay was cut. When animals are on pasture they remove leaves, trample the ground and dung and urinate. If the sward contains different species then there is also selection. And the species the animal selects may vary with its availability. For instance the less white clover that is present the greater the selection pressure on it by sheep.

Stocking weight

It is commonly stated that organic agriculture is extensive and not intensive. When applied to the number of animals kept per unit area (stocking rate), organic farming is assumed to lead to a reduction. The crux of the organic regulations is that productive animals should not be kept short of food at pasture. But how does the farmer know whether the animal is eating as much grass as it needs? Animals eat in relation to their size: so a Welsh Mountain ewe weighing 30 kg will eat less than half the amount annually of a Devon Longwool weighing 80 kg. Thus it is a mistake to define the stocking rate of a field, or a farm, without considering animal size.

The grazing animal has a potential daily intake, which will depend not only on its liveweight but also on its physiological status (e.g. lactating, pregnant, dry). This daily intake can then be summed to outline an approximate annual requirement. If the dry matter, or digestible organic matter, yield of the pasture is known, then an approximate stocking rate can be calculated. For instance, if a 400 kg beef cow with a young calf eats 3.5 t DM per annum and the pasture yield is 5 t DM per ha per annum, then it is reasonable to stock at 600 kg liveweight per ha (excluding the calf), which is equivalent to 1.5 cattle per ha per annum.

At some stages of the year, the future productivity of the pasture may be enhanced by severe defoliation, for instance in the autumn and winter, to ensure that white clover plants are not overtopped by grass. But when a pasture needs grazing down tightly then animal intake is bound to be reduced. Thus, in order to benefit the pasture, animals that are over-fat, or in a store phase, can be grazed at high stocking weights per hectare. In these conditions it is normally better to mob stock for a short period of time rather than use a few animals for several months.

If a pasture has been understocked, with the accumulation of senescent material, or if it contains a high proportion of legumes, then stocking weight may actually be increased under organic conditions and the animals do better than at lower stocking rates on a conventional system with added nitrogen.

Digestibility

Pasture yield can be measured in dry matter per ha per annum, simply by measuring the fresh weight yield and drying the herbage, thus excluding water content, which can be as high as 85% of total yield.

It is vital when calculating feed intake, pasture yield and stocking weight to make sure that all the units are the same. For instance, the amount of silage stored for winter feeding is normally estimated per clamp, probably in fresh weight terms. Silage has a very variable dry matter content (15-35%), so that a forward estimate as to whether there is enough for the winter must take account of dry matter content. Hay, on the other hand, has a very high dry matter (90-95%), so that the amount present is much closer to the dry matter intake of the animal.

Table 12.1.   Digestibility of grassland plants.

Name	Digestible organic matter in dry matter (%)	Metabolisable energy MJ/kg DM	Digestible crude protein g/kg DM
Pasture grass (Non-rotational)	75	12.1	225
Rotational grass	75	12.1	185
Pasture grass, extensive grazing	64	10	124
Winter grazing	63	9.7	101
Post flowering perennial ryegrass	55	8.4	72
Red clover (in flower)	65	10.2	132
White clover (in flower)	57	9.0	152
Grass silage (average)	58	8.8	102
Red clover silage	56	8.8	135
Grass hay (average)	57	8.4	39
Red clover hay	57	8.9	103
Heather	37	6.0	28
Nettles	61	10.4	145
Gorse	45	6.8	44
Elm leaves (dried)	65	10.3	132
Poplar leaves (dried)	53	9.7	72

(from HMSO, 1975)

Digestibility is exactly what it says, namely the proportion of the dry matter that will be digested and used. Thus, of 10 kg of hay of 70% digestibility, 7 kg will be used by the animal and 3 kg will pass through the animal and be excreted.

The higher the digestibility of the grass the more will be eaten, simply because of the bulk factor in the rumen. The other method of describing feeds, apart from protein content, is as metabolisable energy or ME. Again the same relationship holds: the higher the ME value of a forage feed, the more the animal will eat. For instance, a sheep will eat more ME if the grass ME is 10 rather than 7. This is because dry matter intake is close to being a constant. Again, a ewe may eat 2 kg of dry matter of grass of ME value 10, whereas she may only be able to eat 1.8 kg of ME value 7. In the first case, intake is 20 Megajoules, and in the second only 12.6 MJ. The more concentrated the feed, the more can be absorbed.

In a sward young leaves are the most digestible and dead stems the least digestible; values range from 80 down to 30. Sheep are better able to select for leaves of high digestibility than cattle, because of their grazing habit and the smaller size of their mouth. Sheep bite off the leaves, whereas cattle put their tongue round a tuft of grass and pull. When the ingested feed of sheep and cattle grazing the same sward is compared, the digestibility of the sheep's diet is 4 to 5 units higher. This is why cattle are more useful for grazing senescing clumps of coarse grass than sheep; they can't avoid the dead material. Herbs and plants like docks and rushes will also be grazed more readily when they are young and more digestible.

Some typical digestibility and protein values for grassland plants are listed in Table 12.1. The values for grass are slightly arbitrary. The more mature the plant, the lower its digestibility. In the same way, the digestibility of silage and hay will depend on the stage of growth of the crop at the time of harvest. The closer to flowering the cut is made, the lower the D value but the higher the bulk. This will be discussed in more detail in the next chapter.

Although pasture regrowth may have as high a D value as first growth, grass intakes have been shown to be lower at the same digestibility. White clover has a higher intake at a similar digestibility to grass, because of a much lower proportion of cellulose and hemi-cellulose, and its digestibility doesn't fall off as fast as that of grass.

Annual feed budgets for sheep, beef cows and dairy cows are shown in Table 12.2. There are two levels of assumed pasture utilisation, 2 t DM and 6 t DM per ha. One would be typical of grassland with no nitrogen and no legumes: the other assumes a considerable legume proportion.

The table highlights the points made earlier. Small Welsh Mountain ewes can be kept at nearly three times the number of ewes per hectare, compared to half-bred ewes, but when reproductive performance is taken into account, the Welsh ewes will rear 24 lambs per ha on the good pasture, whilst the Half-breds will rear 18 lambs per ha.

Size also influences the relative stocking rates of the Angus and Charolais cattle. The liveweight carried per ha is similar for sheep and cattle, when pasture utilisation is also similar.

On an annual basis the daily intake per animal (whether sheep or cattle) works out at 2.3% of bodyweight. However, daily intake varies with physiological state. A lactating animal will eat almost twice as much as a pregnant animal.

Table 12.2. Annual feed budgets and stocking rates.

Animal Type	Annual Intake (kg DM per ha)	Pasture Utilisation	
		Poor (2t DM/ha)	Good (6t DM/ha)
		Stocking weight (kg liveweight/ha, excluding the offspring)	
30kg Welsh Mountain ewe+ single lamb	250	240 (8)	720 (24)
75kg Halfbred ewe + twins	640	225 (3)	675 (9)
380kg Angus cow + calf	3250	228 (0.6)	684 (1.8)
520kg Charolais cow + calf	4450	208 (0.4)	676 (1.3)
450kg Friesian dairy cow	4200*	225 (0.5)	675 (1.4)

* (+ 1 t conc)

( ) =Stocking rate - animals per ha and assumes that the silage or hay for the winter is made from the same area. Thus at some times grazing stocking rate may be much higher. Pasture utilisation - this is not the amount grown but the amount of dry matter eaten by the animals.

Efficiency of utilisation of grazed grass

Efficiency of utilisation varies with method of calculation and with method of defoliation. If the amount of grass grown is calculated on an annual basis and the amount eaten by the animal is also calculated on an annual basis, then efficiency of utilisation will be between 75 and 85%. If, on the other hand, efficiency is calculated by measuring how much herbage is present to ground level before each grazing and then how much is present after each grazing, then the figure is more likely to be 40-50%. The main reason for the difference is that the amount of herbage below grazing height is excluded when calculating herbage production on an annual basis.

Method of grazing also influences the efficiency of utilisation. Under-grazing will reduce the figure and overgrazing will increase it, and both in turn will affect the amount that is actually grown, as will the grazing system. Rotational grazing will increase the amount of herbage grown, because of a higher leaf area index, which will increase photosynthesis, but will also tend to increase the amount of senescence and wastage. Whereas continuous grazing will reduce the amount grown and also reduce the amount wasted, so this last process will show a higher efficiency of utilisation, but not necessarily a higher amount eaten per ha.

Effect of grazing management on sward composition

This is a particularly important area for the organic farmer because he is not able to spray out plants that he doesn't want. On the other hand, if the hypothesis is correct that there is much larger range of grasses that will give as good a performance in terms of amount of animal production per unit area as perennial ryegrass, then the species of grass present in the sward is not critical. Yorkshire fog, crested dogstail and meadow foxtail will do very well (Chapter 3). Docks, rushes and thistles may be rather less welcome and their control by grazing has been covered in Chapter 10. But weed control by grazing is a slow process. There remains the encouragement of the legume component of the sward. This also was covered in Chapter 4. The main rules for protecting white clover are:

1. Do not graze for long periods with sheep.
2. Do use cattle and goats if possible.
3. Cut the area for hay or silage, once.
4. Ensure that the sward is grazed down closely (3 cm from ground level) going into the winter period of no growth. This enables light to reach the clover stolons and encourages budding and axillary growth in the following spring.

The problem of having too much clover and not enough grass is rarer; but the use of sheep will redress the balance.

Otherwise the sward should be densely packed with tillers and not allowed to get so tall that individual grass plants become tall and senesce.

Systems of grazing

There are three main systems of grazing: set stocking, continuous grazing and rotational grazing. Zero grazing, where the animals are kept indoors and the grass brought to them is not an option for organic farmers.

Set stocking

In this system the animals remain in the same field for the whole grazing season, with no attempt to keep the sward at a suitable height, though extra food may have to be offered at pasture if there is no herbage and the animals' condition is deteriorating. This is a simple, lazy and ineffective method of grazing control.

Continuous grazing

This is a scientific refinement of set stocking. The most important management factor is sward height. Experiments have shown that, for sheep, sward height above ground level should be 5 cm ± 1 cm. This keeps the sward dense and green with a minimum of dead material, without reducing intake significantly. To monitor this height during the early, and fastest growing period of the grazing season, sward height measurements should be taken 2 or 3 times a week. If the sward height gets above 6 cm, then either a moveable fence can be introduced and the area reduced, thus setting up an area for making silage, or more animals can be introduced. If sward height starts to fall below 4 cm or the area becomes very muddy, as might happen with a late or wet spring, then either the number of animals should be reduced by opening up another field or, if no more suitable land is available, by feeding hay or silage at pasture.

Sward height can be increased with time as the season progresses, especially for lambs after weaning. A similar set of management rules can be used for cattle grazing, with sward height centring on 7 cm in the early part of the season.

The main problems with this system are the frequency and number of measurements of sward height, and the rapid reaction that is required by the manager when the sward begins to grow very quickly in the spring.

The benefits are the good animal and sward performance, with a high efficiency of sward utilisation.

Rotational grazing

With rotational grazing the animals are moved through a series of fields. The advantages of this system are:

1) Each field is rested after a period of intensive grazing, which is of benefit to white clover in a sheep system.
2) Leaf area index is kept high, which means more herbage is grown than in set stocking.
3) It is obvious when fields can be taken out of the system for silage or hay.
4) Grazing each area intensively prevents animals from being too selective. Clumps of less popular material are also eaten and not wasted. This is particularly important if the sward contains a great many grass and herb species.

The disadvantages are:

1) Because of the rest period between grazings, the sward can get long and stemmy. This can be avoided by cutting for silage or hay.
2) Intake per animal per day will vary markedly between the first day and the last in the field, particularly if the farmer wishes to keep the sward grazed down tightly.
3) The rest period increases the amount of senescent material.
4) Animals have to be moved on a regular basis.

The results of rotational grazing with ewes and lambs compared with set stocking or continuous grazing are shown in Table 12.3.

In the first experiment, the ewes were Mashams, each with two lambs. They were stocked at 16 ewes per ha. Thus on the rotational grazing, 32 lambs per ha grew at 309 g per head per day from birth to sale. The main points to notice are the much superior lamb and ewe performance with rotational grazing, compared to set-stocking, and the dramatically different effect of type of grazing system on the proportion of clover at the end of the season (5 v 55%). No nitrogen was used in either experiment.

Table 12.3. A comparison of rotational grazing with set stocking or continuous grazing, with ewes and lambs on ryegrass/white clover.

	Experiment 1		Experiment 2	
	Set-stocking	Rotational grazing	Set-stocking	Rotational grazing
Lamb growth rate (g/hd/day)	200	309	209	236
Ewe Liveweight change (kg/ewe)	-10.9	+1.2		
% clover beginning	13	23	2	2
end	5	55	1	15
Silage made (kg DM/ewe)			7	46
Supplement fed (t DM/ha)			1.4	0

(Data from Newton, *et al*, 1985, and Newton *et al*, 1993)

In the second experiment the rotationally-grazed lambs grew faster, there was more clover present (though not as much as in the first experiment), more silage was made and no supplement had to be fed. On the continuously-grazed sward supplement was required to maintain ewe body condition, very little silage was made, there was less clover and the lambs grew more slowly.

There can be little doubt that in a grass/clover sward with no nitrogen, representative of the majority of organic sheep systems, rotational grazing gives better results.

With cattle, on the other hand, no superiority has been shown for rotational grazing either in growth rate or amount of clover present. But cattle select for grass, whereas sheep select for clover.

Effect of sward height on intake

The taller the sward, the longer the individual grass leaf and the more grass a sheep or cow can eat at one bite. As sward height decreases so the animal has to work harder and graze for a longer period each day to obtain its desired ration. Ruminants will not increase their grazing time beyond a certain point; within a 24 hour period they need time to ruminate and sleep as well as graze. So if the sward is too short intake falls.

Within the 24 hour period, approximately 8 hours is required for grazing, 8 hours for ruminating and 8 hours for idling and sleeping.

The only way the sward can be maintained at a tall height, thus facilitating maximum intake, is to reduce the number of animals present. Thus overall productivity per unit area will fall.

The other determinants of intake are quantity of herbage present and digestibility (which has already been discussed). It is likely that there is a correlation between sward height and sward mass. Although sometimes it is possible to have tall open swards with a similar mass to shorter denser ones. In this situation height and leaf size will control intake. For sheep, intake is unlikely to be much reduced at 5 cm from ground level whereas for cattle the optimal height is 7 cm.

Timing of production systems

The daily rate of grass growth is very low during the winter, and rises steadily in spring to reach its fastest rate in May. Thereafter, there is a decline in growth rate until the follwing spring. The further north or the higher the altitude of the farm the more condensed grass growth will be, starting later in the season and finishing earlier. The spring peak of grass growth is accentuated by the use of nitrogen and flattened by the inclusion of white clover.

Systems of sheep and beef production can be adapted to make the maximum and best use or grass. Thus with sheep the main periods for ensuring high intake are the last 4 weeks of pregnancy when the foetuses are growing fastest and the first 4 weeks of lactation when intake is at its highest and a high milk yield is initiated.

In an early lambing system (lambs born December), the best nutrition should be in November, December and January, the worst months for grass growth. This system is therefore the least suitable for the organic farmer requiring the most concentrates and the longest period of housing, particularly for the lambs.

The most usual lambing time (lambs born March/April) is again slightly too early to make the best use of grass. Conserved food and concentrates will certainly be required in late pregnancy and probably in early lactation, particularly if spring growth is delayed.

A late lambing system (lambs born in May) means that the ewes will receive spring grass during late pregnancy and early lactation. In these circumstances it may be possible to reduce the use of conserved feed (hay or silage) to a minimum, and quality will be of less importance because, if it is fed, it will be during mid pregnancy. Providing there is plenty of herbage (grass and clover) per ewe, concentrates can be eliminated altogether.

The disadvantage with late lambing is that it is much harder to get the lambs to an acceptable slaughter weight by September. Late lambing is therefore more reliant on a buoyant store lamb market or on the use of winter forage crops such as turnips, rape or kale.

Lambs that are weaned in July/August from a March/April lambing will grow better on grass/white clover than on grass. The area that contains the most white clover, and the fewest parasitic worms, should be kept for these weaned lambs.

With beef systems, nutritional demand should if possible mimic the grass production curve. This is most easily achieved in their last grazing season. Cattle that are in excess of 300 kg in April can be sent off for slaughter during the summer, thus reducing the stocking rate by August, when grass growth slows down.

Time of calving for beef suckler herds

The choice of calving date determines the overall system of production. The advantage of autumn-calving is that at the autumn sales the calves are older, heavier and therefore more saleable than those from spring-calving cows. However, the extra performance requires extra feed during the winter when cows are lactating.

On the highest hill farms the availability and quality of conserved feeds means that calving should be delayed until the spring. The calves are rather small at the time of sale but production costs are minimised. On lower hill farms and some of the tougher upland farms autumn-calving is still not feasible but feed supplies are sufficient to allow calving during the late winter so that calves are better grown and more saleable. Lowland, and better upland farms are easily capable of producing the quantity and quality of feeds needed to sustain autumn-calving and here the choice depends largely on the availability of buildings and labour.

Summer-calving has been favoured by some people but has not been widely adopted in practice. An advantage of the system is that milk production is established on grazed grass and the cows are re-bred before the winter begins, giving a better chance of high conception rates. In the spring, calves are weaned and given the best grass, while the dry cows are grazed on poorer pastures.

With organic beef systems, cattle are expected to make liveweight gains at grass during the growing season, and are then maintained on cheap forage rations during the winter, which may actually cause loss of liveweight. This means that cattle may be two-and-a-half years old, or older, by the time they reach a suitable weight and finish.

Clean grazing

One of the main problems facing the organic livestock farmer is that of controlling intestinal parasites, mainly because there are no proven herbal or homoeopathic remedies to replace the proprietary drugs, to which the intestinal parasites are becoming resistant. This means that it is important to practice as clean a grazing system as possible, particularly for sheep.

On lowland farms, where the majority of fields can be ploughed up or made into hay or silage, the operation of a clean grazing system is relatively easy. Each field can be grazed by beef and then sheep, after hay (or silage), in a three year rotation. It is crucial that once a field has been grazed by sheep, it should not be grazed by them again for a whole year, in order to allow the parasitic eggs and free-living larvae to die.

Fortunately, the parasites that infect sheep do not infect cattle, and vice versa, with the important exception of *Nematodirus battus*, which infects sheep and young calves. So if a flock is known to be infected with *Nematodirus*, then the cattle that are used to graze the sheep fields subsequently need to be more than six months old.

On hill farms where only a small proportion of the farm is inbye land that can be conserved, then sheep and cattle should be grazed in alternate years on the rough permanent pasture. To do this effectively, it makes sense to have equal numbers of livestock units of sheep and cattle so that they can swap each year. The ratio of sheep to cattle is dependent on the relative size of each, but liveweight can be used as a rough guide and the normally quoted ratio is 6 or 7 sheep to a Friesian cow.

Most hill farms have either all sheep or very many more sheep livestock units than cattle. This makes clean grazing of permanent pasture virtually impossible, and the only tactic then is to graze ewes with twins on the cleaner and better land, and follow them with the ewes with singles. Single lambs, because they consume more milk than twins, eat proportionately less grass.

Efficient grazing of grassland, particularly if it contains plenty of white clover, is best done with sheep and cattle during the same year, and this is a temptation that should be resisted if the sheep are to be kept worm free, and particularly the lambs. Cattle graze higher than sheep, select grass rather than clover, and produce large dung pats. The herbage grows lushly round the dung, and cattle are reluctant to graze too close because of the taint, whereas sheep will eat closer to the dung, thus avoiding wastage.

The value of sheep grazing is that they graze the sward tightly, thus encouraging a well tillered sward, but they select clover rather than grass. They will also graze much further into the winter without poaching the land beyond recovery. If land that is known to be infested needs grazing, then this is best done by dry ewes and not by weaned lambs.

Early bite

There are three ways round the problem of early bite for the organic farmer. One is to lamb later, or to turn the cattle out later, but this lengthens the indoor winter feeding period. The second is to experiment with the method suggested by Newman Turner, of covering the pastures with a thin layer of straw, thus encouraging growth earlier by warming up the soil. The third method is to grow a specialist early crop such as rye.

Topping

Topping pastures is useful to encourage rank pasture to produce young and nutritious leaves. It also serves to control weeds such as thistles and docks, if carried out at the right time. Topping shouldn't be performed when the overall pasture is too long, because the topped material will create too thick a layer and smother the grass underneath, although it is possible to graze the topped sward and remove heavy material this way.

Winter management

Winter management has already been mentioned in relation to white clover. But the same principles apply to grass swards. If swards are allowed to go into the winter in too dense a condition, then there will be increased senescence and the sward will become choked. Sward height at the end of the grass growing season (Nov/Dec) should be 3 cm. Because the amount of light for photosynthesis is reduced during the winter months, the grass plant can only support a smaller canopy.

If stock are overwintered outside, then excessive poaching damage should be avoided both from the point of view of the sward and the animal. This means that winter stocking rates should be about one third of those in the summer.

Grass can be grazed until the middle of February without affecting the subsequent conservation cut of silage, providing about 3 cm of material are left.

Fencing

To obtain proper control of grazing management, stock-proof fencing is essential. Where fields are very large and a rotational system of management is required then portable electric fencing is effective, even with sheep, which are much harder to control than cattle.

Reference

H.M.S.O. 1975 *Energy Allowances and Feeding Systems for Ruminants.* Technical Bulletin 33, HMSO, London, 88 pp.
Newton, J.E., Laws, J.A., Woods, M.R. and Rawlins, F. (1993) *The effect of grazing management on lowland sheep production* (in press).
Newton, J.E., Wilde, R.M. and Betts, J.E. (1985) *Research and Development in Agriculture,* 2, 1-6.

Chapter 13

Forage conservation

The concept of sustainability infers that fertility should neither be imported nor exported. With conserved forages such as hay, sustainability is hard to achieve because of the variation in annual rainfall which causes considerable variation in grass production.

The importance of forage conservation varies with the length of the winter feeding period. Thus dairy cow production in northern latitudes has a much greater reliance on conserved winter products (likely to be for 6 months of the year) compared with sheep systems in the milder south west where small quantities of hay may be needed for only one or two months in the winter.

The organic farmer has the additional complication, should he miscalculate his winter feed requirements, that because of the relative scarcity of organic land, organic hay is expensive and in short supply.

Finally, as stocking rate on the farm is increased, so the pressure on the available grassland is increased during the grazing season; but, at the same time, more stock have to be budgeted for during the winter months, thus increasing the amount of land needed to make sufficient conservation. The organic farmer, because of his dedication to a sustainable system, must, therefore, ensure that hay and silage is given a high priority.

General principles

The objective of forage conservation can be defined as "the production of a stable product of adequate nutritive value with the minimum of loss and at a reasonable capital and labour cost!"

Grass varies greatly in composition at different stages of its growth. The features that particularly affect conservation are the moisture content of the grass and its content of soluble carbohydrate and crude protein (Chapter 12). Young leafy grass contains over 80% water, and the dry matter can contain 20% crude protein and up to 30% of sugars and other water-soluble carbohydrates. Approximately 75% of this dry matter is digestible by ruminants. Some grass species, especially the ryegrasses, are naturally higher in sugar content than others such as cocksfoot, timothy and the clovers; sugar contents are generally highest in late afternoon, and they tend to be lowest in crops heavily fertilised with nitrogen; conversely, such crops have a higher crude protein content.

The organic farmer then, using no bag nitrogen, has to worry less about sugar content and more about protein level, unless he conserves fields with a high level of clover.

113

As the grass crop matures, the protein content falls rapidly and the fibre content gradually increases. At first, the sugar content rises, particularly as stem is formed before and shortly after first-ear emergence, but as the crop becomes more mature its sugar content also falls, and it rapidly becomes less digestible. However, this is the period of most rapid growth of the crop, when yield is increasing fast. At the same time the moisture content falls, which is important when considering conservation.

Losses in conservation

As soon as the crop is cut, changes take place that can easily lead to deterioration and loss.

Physical losses can occur during cutting, crimping, pick-up by the forage harvester or baler, or through losses from baled hay during handling, and losses of hay or silage trodden into bedding by stock. Waste at the top and sides of silos and moulding of hay can also be significant sources of loss. Where these losses are mainly of leaf material, as may occur with lucerne and red clover, they can lead to an appreciable decrease both in protein content and digestibility.

Respiration losses occur because the plant continues to respire after it is cut, as long as it still contains a reasonable amount of moisture (over 30%) and air is present. Heat is produced during respiration, and if this cannot be removed rapidly, the temperature of the mass rises and this may lead to 'heated' brown hay and 'over-heated' dark brown silage.

Fermentation, which also produces losses, is the process of chemical breakdown of plant material by micro-organisms - bacteria and moulds. It is the key process in silage making, where the aim is to create conditions so that the bacteria present on forage ferment the sugars in the forage to produce acids (mainly lactic acid) which then 'pickle' the forage and stop further bacterial action.

The extent of fermentation loss varies with the type of crop, and particularly with its moisture content. It is negligible in dry crops (below 15% moisture content, e.g. hay) and of the order of 5% in crops of 20-65% moisture content, and progressively greater in wetter crops. Fermentation loss is most serious in wet crops of high legume content, where an insufficient concentration of lactic acid is produced, because then fermentation is prolonged, secondary products are formed, and the silage can be smelly, unpalatable and have reduced feed value.

When the crop is cut, the cells collapse and liquid escapes. The amount released will depend on the moisture content and the pressure applied. Generally, liquid cannot be pressed out of stored grass of less than 65% moisture content. Because water is one of the products of fermentation, a high fermentation loss during ensilage can increase effluent loss.

Soluble components of the crop may be washed out by rain, either from the cut crop in the field during wilting for hay making and silage, or by rain washing through the silage which is inefficiently top-sealed.

About 70% of the protein in grass is generally in digestible form but, particularly where there is over-heating during conservation, the digestibility of this protein can be reduced to a very low level.

Moulds

These occur if the product is inefficiently conserved, e.g. the hay is too moist or the silage is not acid enough. In certain circumstances, toxins (produced by the moulds) can cause digestive upsets in stock.

Vitamins

Grass is an important source of B-carotene which the animal can convert into vitamin A. The action of the sun's rays, of excessive amounts of air, and of 'over-heating' cause the destruction of most of the carotene in grass.

Haymaking

Most of the moisture present in the grass is removed in the field. The crop is baled at about 25% moisture content when it is safe to stack, where it 'cures' down to about 14-15% moisture content. This curing is due to continued slight respiration and consequent heating of the damp hay; this sets up a current of warm air through the stack, which removes the final moisture.

The easiest crops to make into hay are very mature dry crops which cure readily by sun and wind. However, even when well made, this hay will be of low digestibility and protein value.

On the other hand, leafy grass of high digestibility is difficult to make into hay in the field, even with tripods or racks. A compromise has to be made between ease of making and quality and this is best achieved by cutting when the grass is just beginning to flower.

Silage

Making good silage depends on the production of sufficient lactic acid to 'pickle' the crop. In general, the wetter the silage the greater the extent of fermentation and the greater the acidity of the silage. If there is insufficient sugar, or too much water in the crop, or both, then undesirable micro-organisms will multiply and produce butyric acid, which makes an unpleasant silage.

Certain rules must be observed to ensure as high a sugar content as possible:
1. Don't cut at too immature a stage of crop growth.
2. Cut in the afternoon.
3. Wilt the crop in the field.
4. Increase the sugar by adding molasses.
5. In wet seasons bacterial silage additives can be used.
6. Chop the crop short to release the sugar quickly.

Typical dry matter and sugar levels in grass are shown in Table 13.1.

Table 13.1 Effect of stage of growth and weather on dry matter levels and sugar content in grass.

Weather	Leafy		Ear Emergence		Stemmy	
	DM %	Sugar %	DM %	Sugar %	DM %	Sugar%
Sunny	16-20	2-4	18-25	2.5-5	22-30	3-6
Cloudy	14-18	1.5-3	16-20	2-3.5	20-24	2.5-4.5
Showery	10-14	1-2	12-16	1.5-3	18-21	2-3.5

Targets to aim for are 25% dry matter and 3% sugars in the fresh crop weight. With wilting the general rule is to harvest the day after mowing. If the weather is dry, an adequate wilt should be achieved and the target of 25% dry matter reached. In poor weather there is no point in waiting longer than 24 hours, because the loss of sugars due to plant respiration can exceed the loss of water from the crop, making the material more liable to secondary fermentation.

A method of estimating dry matter % in the field is shown in Table 13.2. The procedure involves taking a handful of grass from the swath, rolling it into a ball and squeezing for one minute.

Table 13.2 Dry matter percentage

		Dry matter
1.	Juice drips from the ball during squeezing	< 25%
2.	Ball retains shape when released, no juice	25-35%
3.	Ball unfolds slowly	35-45%
4.	Ball unfolds quickly, grass breaks	> 45%

Air must be prevented from getting into the silage mass because otherwise it becomes very hot, and above 55°C the protein becomes increasingly less digestible. Wilted silage is particularly prone to overheating. Because of this risk, heavily wilted crops are normally ensiled in tower silos.

As with hay, the type of crop usually ensiled is one that is intermediate in terms of maturity (digestibility) and protein content.

Crops for conservation

Grasses and legumes contain different amounts of sugar. For instance, cocksfoot has less sugar than perennial ryegrass. But the effect of adding large quantities of nitrogen is to reduce the amount of soluble carbohydrate. Thus, under a regime of no nitrogen fertiliser, cocksfoot may ensile well.

Legumes cause further problems for ensiling. This is because legumes have a considerably higher buffering capacity (i.e. resistance to acidification) than grass. Therefore they require a higher initial level of sugar to ensure a good fermentation. It follows that the choice of companion grass for a legume may be important.

As herbage passes from the leaf vegetative stage to the 'juicy stem' phase, it becomes increasingly easier to conserve, although it is sometimes difficult to wilt Italian ryegrass and red clover. The tetraploid Italian ryegrasses present peculiar difficulties, due to their low dry matter content.

The ranking of crops for ensilability is shown in Table 13.3, from (1) very easy to preserve well without an additive, to (12) very difficult.

The quality of conserved herbage depends on inherent differences between species and varieties. Simplicity in management and predictability for conservation are important aspects, and therefore a primary cut from single varieties of different growth rhythms offers many advantages. However, if the nutritive quality of the conserved product is the main consideration, a mixed grass sward containing legumes, is more desirable.

Clover will supply nutritive constituents, both organic and mineral, which are deficient in some species and varieties of grass. There is evidence to show that less than 20% clover, when incorporated in conserved fodder, can have a profound influence on animal production. The most difficult silage to make will often be of greatest value nutritionally.

Table 13.3   **Ensilability ranking.**

1.	Maize
2.	Whole crop cereals
3.	Italian and hybrid ryegrass
4.	Perennial ryegrass
5.	Bromegrass
6.	Timothy/meadow fescue
7.	Cocksfoot
8.	Permanent pasture
9.	Arable silage containing legumes
10.	Grass/clover
11.	Red clover
12.	Lucerne

from Wilkinson (1990)

A score card has been produced (Table 13.4) specifically for deciding when an additive is likely to help preserve silage in good condition. Organic farmers may only use molasses, to increase sugar content, and some biological additives selected for their ability to produce lactic acid. Some contain enzymes to break down hemicellulose or cellulose in the plant cell wall fraction, to generate extra fermentable sugars. Others contain bacteria which are known to ferment cell wall material. Some contain fermentable substrate in addition to bacterial inocula and enzymes. Looking at Table 13.4 there is a row headed 'fertiliser N'. As N use increases, so the risk of making poor quality silage also increases, because of reduced sugar content. So at least the organic silage maker always has the advantage of scoring 3 in this slot.

Crop 1 would present no problems, but much greater care would be needed with crop 2, and the addition of molasses would be essential. Note the very strong effect of the weather on the score card.

118

Table 13.4 Scorecard for assessing risk of poor preservation of silage

Score	5	4	3	2	1	Your Score
Species	Italian ryegrass Maize	Perennial ryegrass	Other grasses	Grass/clover	Lucerne Red clover	
Stage of growth		Stemmy	Ear emergence	Leafy		
Fertiliser N (kg/ha/cut)			<50	50-100	>100	
Forage Harvester	Metered chop	Double chop	Flail	Forage wagon	Big baler*	
Weather	Sunny		Cloudy		Showery	
Season			Spring+ Summer		Autumn	
					Total Score	

Score	Risk of poor preservation
Above 20	low
15-20	Medium
Below 15	high

* Big bales left unwrapped in field for a few days = 1
Big bales wrapped immediately = 4

Taking two contrasting organic crop situations as examples:

Crop 1		Crop 2	
Other grasses	3	Grass/clover	2
Stemmy	4	Ear emergence	3
No fertiliser	3	No fertiliser	3
Double-chop	4	Forage wagon	2
Sunny	5	Showery	1
Summer	3	Autumn	1
	22		**12**

Yield and Digestibility

The important relationship between yield and quality has already been mentioned. Basically, total yield of dry matter increases with the length of time a crop is allowed to grow, whereas the digestibility of the forage is declining. Animals will prefer more highly digestible food. The exact relationship between yield and digestibility varies from crop to crop.

In the North-East, crop growth begins later in spring and early-maturing grasses are particularly affected. Once growth is under way the change in yield and digestibility are even more rapid than in the south. In general, as yield increases progressively in spring, digestibility (D-value or DOMD, the content of digestible organic matter in the dry matter) falls - from more than 70% early in April to less than 55% in late June. After late May, the yield of digestible organic matter is hardly increasing at all and digestibility is falling all the time. It therefore makes no sense to delay cutting after this date.

The digestibility of white clover falls at a much slower rate than that of grass. In the same period (April to late June) that the digestibility of perennial ryegrass falls by 20 units, the digestibility of S100 white clover falls by only 5 units (75% to 70%). Thus, a mixture of white clover and a late grass such as timothy can be cut much later, at a reasonably high digestibility.

Feed value of conserved grass

Conserved grass is fed to all kinds of livestock, but what they require from it differs considerably. Dry cows and store cattle mainly need bulk. Productive stock, such as lactating dairy cows, and to a lesser extent pregnant sheep, need better quality food. Maximum use of hay and silage for these animals would reduce the need for concentrates , which is particularly important for organic farmers who can only feed 40% of the daily requirement as concentrates to a ruminant animal and also if the price of the concentrate is high. With efficient conservation, and cutting at the right stage, the digestibility values of the crop and the conserved product should be almost the same, and not below a D value of 65.

However, the intake of silage is reduced if it is very wet, so wilting is important. Rations can contain several different conserved forages, which are complementary. For instance, whole-crop cereal or maize, which have a high energy concentration but a low protein content, can be balanced with a legume silage or field beans which have lower energy and higher protein levels.

Dairy cows

1. The cow has a large appetite, varying from 11 kg dry matter a day for small breeds, not lactating, to 18 kg of dry matter per day for large breeds, and animals giving high milk yields.
2. This appetite varies during the course of lactation and pregnancy.
3. Hammer-milled roughages are unsuited to dairy cows, as they result in low butterfat levels in the milk.
4. Protein requirements are 16% crude protein in the dry matter.

Overall digestibility of the diet can therefore vary considerably with stage of lactation. At peak lactation, digestibility should be 65-70 D, whereas at the end of lactation a D value of 55 is satisfactory. It is therefore unrealistic to produce a standard diet for dairy cows to feed ad lib throughout the indoor period.

Fattening beef cattle.

These animals have different requirements from dairy cows.
1. Their appetite is smaller, depending on size (7-11 kg DM).
2. Appetite increases steadily with age and weight.
3. Protein levels of 12 to 14% are satisfactory.
It is easier therefore to standardise diets for beef production.

Sheep

Hay or silage of high quality (65 D or above) can be fed alone to pregnant ewes with twins, to produce lambs of satisfactory birth weight. But, if silage is being fed, then ensure that the best silage is kept for the final weeks. If you are unsure about the quality of the hay or silage, or about the intake of the silage, then concentrates should be offered as well.

Foggage

Foggage is the accumulation of mature herbage in the autumn. In a sense it is conservation without cutting. But the quality of the material will be low, and utilisation can be a problem during wet weather, on land that is not freely drained.

A farmer needs to look at the various methods of conservation, silage, hay, barn-drying, and grass drying and see how they fit into his overall system of farming. Conservation should have priority over grazing in the spring for dairy cows, but not for sheep.

Reference

Wilkinson J.M. 1990 *Silage UK,* 6th Edition. Chalcombe Publications, Kingston, Canterbury, 175pp.

Chapter 14

Converting to organic grassland.

Various attempts have been made to calculate whether organic farming is likely to be more profitable than conventional farming. The key issues are: the level of management and the size of the premium for organic produce. Each issue then breaks down into topics such as:

1)   Whether organic farming is more demanding and whether it is more labour intensive.

2)   Whether organic producers should receive a premium, on the grounds that they are operating a `better' method of farming. 'Better' here means safer food, better soil structure, being more sensitive to animal welfare and less accumulation of expensive surpluses of beef, milk or butter.

If producers receive a product premium and if this extra money is passed on by the retail chain, then organic food will be more expensive and therefore less likely to be bought by the consumer. Does this not defeat part of the object of the exercise? If the food is safer (less risk from chemicals or hormones) and possibly of better quality (less fat) then shouldn't it retail at the same price, to benefit a greater proportion of the population?

The conversion period

There is a two-year conversion period between the last application of fast-acting fertiliser or use of pesticide or herbicide and qualification for the organic symbol. During this period, produce cannot be sold as 'symbol standard' but there are some outlets for 'in conversion' products, which offer a small premium. The conversion period can cause confusion, because of the change in farming methods. Different methods of farming have to be learnt and put into practice. On large farms it is likely that part of the flock or herd will be organic and part conventional, if only because it is difficult to organise the conversion of all the grassland, including temporary leys, in a short period of time. But if this happens, the organic sheep will have to be dipped separately in a non organo-phosphate dip, and be fed and housed separately. All this needs extra organisation. In two European countries, Sweden and Germany, a grant is available to farmers wishing to convert, and this has increased the number of farmers converting to organic agriculture.

The fully converted farm

In a comparison of gross margin costings (Younie, 1989), the organic farm shows a saving in fertiliser and veterinary costs and a possible premium for the product, a reduction in stocking rate, less conserved silage/hay and a slower animal growth rate because of less concentrates being fed. Less concentrate input may be balanced by the higher purchase price of organic cereals, if grown on the same farm.

Fertiliser cost and stocking rate

The saving in fertiliser cost is governed by the fertiliser price and by the farming enterprise. For a conventional beef enterprise (Younie, 1989), a forage cost of £150 per ha is quoted, and this covers 270 kg N/ha/annum and 75 kg P_2O_5 and 150 kg K_2O per ha per annum. This works out at £35 per head.

This is more nitrogen than the average beef farmer applies (closer to 100 kg N/ha) but the stocking rate is also higher. Taking the average figure of 100 kg nitrogen application per ha for beef and sheep farms, then the cost is likely to be about £55 per ha. Added to this is the cost of sprays against weeds and pests. The organic farmer is likely to apply lime, but so will the conventional farmer. This means that the organic beef and sheep farmer is likely to make a saving of about £50 per ha on forage costs.

Assuming that the beef and sheep farmer is grazing mainly permanent pasture, then there is no cost of seeds. The organic farmer can also expect a greater contribution from white clover, because he is using no artificial nitrogen. Under these circumstances on a fully-converted farm, it is possible from the forage point of view that the organic farmer need not reduce his stocking rate at all, compared to when he was applying fast-acting fertilisers.

Animal health

A reduction in the numbers of beef animals or sheep per unit area will reduce the number of parasite eggs deposited per unit area. But if clean grazing methods for reducing the risk of parasitic infection are carried out (Chapter 12), then this risk should be minimal. The claim that animals reared according to organic standards are healthier than conventional animals is based on ensuring that nutrition is always adequate, and that the diet is varied, with attention being paid to trace elements and minerals. Attention to these factors does not mean a lower stocking rate at pasture for organic animals. Other aspects stressed in the organic standards include the provision of plenty of space for stock when housed, exercise and fresh air, clean bedding, water and no more than 40% concentrates in the diet for ruminants. None of this impinges on grazing stocking rate.

To summarise: there seems no reason why organic beef and sheep enterprises should produce fewer animals per ha than conventional beef and sheep farmers using 100 kg of N per ha, provided that:

1. the organic pastures contain plenty of clover;
2. size of the animal and the amount of herbage present is taken into account, and
3. a clean grazing policy is carried out.

The situation with dairy cows is likely to be different, firstly because fertiliser application is likely to be much higher (300 - 400 kg N per ha per annum) and secondly because there is much greater dependence on temporary pastures. A good grass/clover sward should yield 7 t of utilisable dry matter per ha per annum, grass with 300 kg of N is likely to yield 10 t of utilisable dry matter per annum. This suggests that the organic farmer will be able to stock his cows at 0.7 of his previous stocking rate. In terms of milk yield, research suggests that dairy cows receiving a high proportion of white clover in their diet, compared with just perennial ryegrass, can increase their milk yield by 10%. Milk per ha on the organic farm will therefore be reduced by 0.23 compared with the conventional dairy herd, but the cost of fertiliser will be £150 per ha less.

As far as the grass rotation is concerned, the organic standards recommend a long grass break in an arable rotation. This will have implications for the dairy : cereal ratio. Finally, because the organic farmer must rely on white clover for his production, his seeds mixture will contain more legume and be more expensive, but then if his grass is down for longer he will incur lower reseeding costs.

Forage conservation

When an organic beef system was compared with a conventional system (Younie, 1989), the yield of first cut silage over 3 years averaged 5.94 for the organic and 6.66 t dry matter per ha for the conventional system. Both beef and milk production require a longer period indoors (6 months) compared with sheep (0 to 3 months). A reduction of 10% in available conserved forage dry matter means that purchased feed costs are likely to increase or that a larger area needs to be set aside for hay or silage in the organic beef or dairy system.

Concentrates

The recommendation in the organic standards is to keep the amount of concentrate feed as low as possible, without affecting animal welfare (body condition and litter weight at birth). Almost by definition, the organic farmer will feed less concentrates per animal but at the moment he is likely to have to pay more per tonne. The organic farmer who feeds a concentrate must know exactly what is in the mix and that it does not contain feedstuffs of animal origin or that have been extracted using a solvent process.

Veterinary costs

The cost of veterinary treatment is likely to be less on the organic farm, mainly because the organic farmer cannot use routine medication. This does not mean that his animals should suffer. If there is no effective alternative cure, then he should use standard veterinary products but only in the case of a known farm problem and on the individual animal affected.

Replacement costs

The replacement of animals forms a significant proportion of costs in systems of livestock production involving breeding: for instance, dairy herds, beef suckler systems and ewe flocks. Newman Turner (1956) was emphatic that cows kept on a sustainable organic system would have fewer reproductive problems; Dinah Williams (1991) contrasted the number of calvings per cow 50 years ago, which was likely to be 10, with the average figure of only 3 calvings per cow in 1991. Unfortunately there are no data proving that breeding animals on an organic farm include fewer barren animals or have shorter parturition to conception intervals, or that they continue healthy production for longer, but it may well be the case. This topic deserves scientific examination.

Labour

Gross margin costings take no account of labour costs. If realistic labour and rent costs are applied to farming enterprises, then what appears to be a comfortable profit may well become an anxious loss. A high proportion of organic farms are family farms with little or no outside help. In looking at organic production it is essential to assume that the family receive an adequate income from the farm; otherwise it is not sustainable.

No figure is yet available as to the extra labour costs on an organic farm. But weed control, for instance, is more time consuming and slower; animal care is also likely to take more time, mainly because the remedies are slower.

Premium for organic produce

There are two main points of view on the case for organic producers receiving a premium price for their products. The first is that if organic methods are better for the soil and the products are safer and better for the consumer, then the government should ensure that the soil is not eroded, the rivers are not polluted and wildlife is not poisoned, by paying farmers to convert to organic methods. If this also helped to reduce over-production, in a more sensible manner than set-aside, then this would be an additional benefit. If the farmer was paid to convert and was also guaranteed a minimum and reasonable price for his products, then it is possible that organic food need not cost the consumer more money, and a greater part of the population be able to change to a healthier diet.

The second argument is that in a market economy the consumer should be willing to pay more for organic food because it is safer, better and with more emphasis on animal welfare. This is already the case in farm gate sales and possibly with some butchers. It is when supermarkets are involved that problems arise. The main argument in favour of selling organic food in supermarkets is that this is the only way that it will become a significant part of the nation's food and so contribute to encouraging more farmers to switch to organic production. The problem is the number of middlemen involved, and the power of the supermarkets compared to the sparse numbers of organic producers in any one area. The supermarket quickly becomes the controller of organic prices and volumes, potentially to the detriment of the producer.

The question of what premium the organic producer should receive is impossible to answer. Does the conventional farmer receive an adequate price for his produce at the moment? It would be better if the return to organic producers was based on their costs plus a profit margin, rather than adding a sum to the conventional price. This would take out the comparison with conventional farming and increase the chance that organic agriculture be studied in its own right.

Demand for organic produce

The related question to the cost of producing organic meat or milk is the question of its cost to the consumer. Survey data (Lampkin, 1991) show that the demand for organic produce is very cost-sensitive. When organic food is double the price of conventional food, then only 5% of consumers are prepared to pay such a huge premium. It is only when the premium falls to 15% above the price of conventional food that the big increase in demand occurs. If the price is the same then, according to Lampkin, 85% of consumers will choose organic produce. The demand for organic food in the shops is consumer-led, but only if the price differential is no greater than 15%.

Predictions have also been made of the growth in consumption of organic meat. The most likely scenario (Coopers and Lybrand Deloitte, 1990) suggests a rise from 0.3% of the conventional market in 1990 to 2% in 1995 and 5% by the year 2000. The predicted growth figures for milk products are identical. Annual sales of lamb in Britain amount to 320,000 t; 0.3% of this is 960, 2% is 6400 and 5% is 16,000 t. In a survey of organic farmers carried out in 1990 (Newton, 1990) the average flock size on symbol farms was 148 ewes. Assuming that each ewe sells 1.5 lambs then the number of lambs sold per farm = 222. If each lamb has a carcass weight of 17 kg, the weight of organic lambs sold per symbol holding farm = 3.7 t. To meet the current demand for 960 t, 259 farms are required. This would rise to 1729 farms in 1995 and 4324 farms in 2000. At the moment there are 150 symbol holders for sheep, not enough even to supply the current demand of 0.3% of the conventional market.

The other problem, exacerbated by the small number of producers, is that the supermarkets require an even supply throughout the year. There is no sign that organic production of lamb differs in pattern from that of conventional lamb. Thus the supply in April, May and June is very low.

Similar calculations can be made for beef, dairy, pigs and poultry. At the time of writing (1992) the number of symbol holders for beef is similar to that of sheep, with dairy, pigs and poultry being very much less. In the case of pigs and poultry, the problem with conversion is the high proportion of expensive organic cereal in their rations. Without a hefty premium this makes organic pigs and poultry uneconomic. From the welfare point of view this is unfortunate, because pigs and poultry production have suffered most from intensive methods of housing and nutrition.

National consequences of organic agriculture

Those involved in intensive farming claim that if there was a substantial shift to organic farming then the people of Britain would starve. It is a sobering thought, but untrue. One may ask: is there a national policy, which sets out how many million ha are required for cereal production, how many million litres of milk, how many head of beef, how many million sheep, eggs, and pigs? The answer is no, unless it is kept out of sight somewhere in the Ministry of Agriculture. The Common Agricultural Policy (CAP) seeks to impose milk quotas and a national flock size, above which payment will not be made. This policy is formulated to prevent too many millions of green ecus being spent to support agriculture in the European Community (EC). The background is one of overproduction, hence the policy of set-aside, in which farmers are paid to allow land to lie idle.

At the same time there is little attempt to protect British organic farmers from price competition from abroad. This competition will reduce the price of food to the consumer, but it will be at the expense of the farmers' profit margin. For milk, beef and lamb, grassland farmers in Britain and Ireland are well-placed to compete with other EC countries because of the relatively favourable climate for grass growth. Thus in Britain the number of grass growing days varies from over 300 in Cornwall to under 200 in East Anglia: a longer growing season than in other European countries.

Milk production would decline to about 80% of its current level, if all dairy farmers became organic. We have already had several years of milk quotas, imposed by

Brussels to reduce milk production, so this might not be too disastrous nationally; and if there was a small premium for organic milk it would not be financially crippling for the organic dairy farmer. There would be a reduction in fertiliser costs.

The switch from conventional to organic beef and sheep production need not lead to any reduction in the national beef herd and sheep flock, nor to using extra land, provided white clover is used to replace bag nitrogen. So, even in the extreme scenario of all milk and meat being produced organically, there is no sign of likely starvation.

It is also worth considering the argument that set-aside land may be much harder to put back into agricultural production than land that has been farmed more extensively under organic conditions.

Organic cereal production would reduce yield both per hectare and per farm, because more of the farm would be under grass and clover at any one time. In the long run, this switch would be beneficial in reducing nitrate levels in the water supply, which is already a problem in the eastern counties, and also in maintaining and improving soil structure, thus reducing soil erosion. The central theme of organic agriculture is sustainable production: so that our descendants benefit from husbandry and are not left with increasing problems and a denuded landscape.

Finally, the reduction in the use of vaccines, anthelmintics, antibiotics and growth promoters has led some veterinarians to paint a picture of ravaging disease with a series of epidemics, if organic agriculture becomes more widespread. This will not happen because good animal health and welfare is paramount for organic farmers: they may use conventional protection if alternative methods don't exist; and the emphasis on balanced nutrition, exercise and minimising stress has already surprised many farmers converting from conventional to organic production by the way it has reduced disease and health problems.

Conclusions

1. The goal of 2% organic food produced in Britain by the year 2000 is realistic and achievable.
2. Organic agriculture needs and deserves government support for the process of conversion and also for research and development.
3. Research and development are needed in the case of organic grassland, especially to define its potential utilised output (which includes white clover) and also to indicate how to realise this potential.
4. In this book the principles of organic grassland farming have been outlined and discussed. The aim throughout has been to encourage the organic farmer to apply these priciples effectively, with a view to achieving improved output and higher profitability.

References

Coopers Lybrand Deloitte 1990 *Going Organic* 21pp.

Lampkin, N. 1991 *Organic Farming,* Farming Press, Ipswich, 701pp.

Younie, D. 1989 *Eighteen-month beef production: organic and intensive systems compared,* 41-54. in: *Organic Meat Production in the '90s.* (Eds. Chamberlain, A.T., Walsingham, J.M. and Stark, B.A.) Chalcombe Publications, Kingston, Canterbury, 85pp.